It's another great book from CGP...

This fantastic CGP book is packed with practice for
Spelling, Punctuation and Grammar (or SPaG for short),
which is worth 5% of the marks in some GCSE subjects.

There's a huge range of questions covering all the important skills, plus
proofreading tasks to help you spot mistakes in the exams.

Once you've worked through all these, you'll be in a great position
to pick up those crucial marks — and you might even find
that SPaG comes in handy in real life too...

CGP — still the best! ☺

Our sole aim here at CGP is to produce the highest quality books —
carefully written, immaculately presented and dangerously close to being funny.

Then we work our socks off to get them out to you
— at the cheapest possible prices.

CONTENTS

CONTENTS

Published by CGP

Editors:
Heather Gregson
Lucy Loveluck
Heather McClelland
Sabrina Robinson

With thanks to Matt Topping for the proofreading.

ISBN: 978 1 78294 219 1

Clipart from Corel®
Printed by Elanders Ltd, Newcastle upon Tyne.

Based on the classic CGP style created by Richard Parsons.

Plurals

Q1 Write the **plural forms** of the words below in the correct box:

version	character	religion	speech	conflict	branch	process

Add 's'	**Add 'es'**

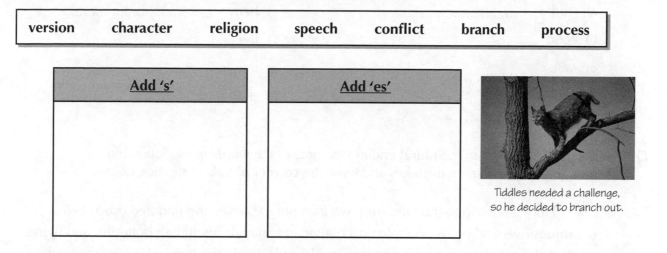

Tiddles needed a challenge,
so he decided to branch out.

Q2 Add '-s' or '-es' to the words in italics to make them plural:

a) Mrs Jefferson asked Paul to hand out the *atlas*..... and the *compass*..... to the *pupil*.......

b) *Taxi*..... to the station charge *passenger*..... extra for transporting bulky *item*.......

c) Conditions in the *trench*..... were terrible for the *soldier*.......

d) Please take these *box*..... to the top of the *stair*..... and put any dirty *sock*..... in the wash.

e) Countries make *alliance*..... with *nation*..... which share their *idea*.......

f) *Church*..... often have several *crucifix*..... on display around their *altar*.......

g) Coastal *area*..... attract *tourist*..... who want to visit beautiful *beach*.......

Q3 Circle the words below that have a **plural** that ends in '-ies':

nationality   duty   holiday   tendency   alloy

abbey   policy   comedy   subtlety   navy

Q4 Work out the **plurals** of the words in the box, then use
the plurals to fill in the **gaps** in the sentences below:

country	valley	delay	treaty	journey	charity	survey	family

a) The train crash caused .... to all .... from Manchester.

b) Geologists carried out .... on two V-shaped .... in Wales.

c) Leaders of many different .... signed both peace ....

d) There are several .... which help .... to adopt children.

Plurals

Q5 Write down the **plural forms** of these words:

a) studio ....

b) echo ....

c) ratio ....

d) potato ....

e) hero ....

f) logo ....

g) tomato ....

h) solo ....

Q6 There are mistakes in the **plural endings** of some of the words in the following passage. **Underline** the mistakes and write the **correct plurals** in the box below.

During our trip to the rainforest, we took our canoeses and paddled down two enormous rivers. We saw a whole host of different animals, including butterflys and flying foxs. In the evening, we watched some monkies playing in the trees whilst we camped by the riverbank. Clara had packed everything we needed, from firelighters and sleeping bags, to cards and dominos for our evening entertainment. Julie, however, had packed some silly things — she brought along two portable radioes, and she packed her favourite dresses and her dancing shoes because she thought there would be some discoes nearby.

Q7 Write the **plural forms** of the words in italics on the dotted lines:

a) The *thief* escaped down the *cliff*. .... , ...

b) The *midwife* saved their *life*. .... , ...

c) The *chef* sharpened the *knife*. .... , ...

d) The *wolf* chased the *calf*. .... , ...

Q8 Work out the **plurals** of the words in the box, then use the plurals to fill in the **gaps** in the sentences below:

half	belief	motif	tariff

a) Understanding mobile phone .... can be very complicated.

b) A person's religious .... affect their behaviour.

c) Two .... make a whole.

d) The walls of the temple were covered with colourful ....

Plurals

Q9   Complete the sentences below using the correct **plural form** of the word in brackets.

    a) In 1914, Britain had around 700 000 .... *(man)* in its army.

    b) Snowdon is about 3 560 .... *(foot)* high.

    c) Some .... *(child)* use Advent calendars to count off the days until Christmas.

    d) Before the 1960s, most of the food .... *(person)* ate was grown in the UK.

    e) Students must meet several .... *(criterion)* to join the society.

Q10   Circle the **most appropriate** word in italics to complete the sentences below correctly:

    a) *Womans / Women* gained more freedom in Britain in the 1920s.

    b) There is a story in the Bible about 5 *loaves / loafs* and 2 fish.

    c) In the trenches, soldiers had to live alongside rats and *lice / louces*.

    d) Turkeys or *gooses / geese* form a traditional part of the Christmas meal for many people.

    e) There are two *Jamess / Jameses* among Jesus's disciples.

    f) The Romans and the Greeks used toothpicks to clean their *tooths / teeth*.

    g) The *Kennedys / Kennedies* were a famous American family.

Q11   Circle the words below that stay the same in the **plural**.

aircraft	history	priest	offspring	globe
desire	species	moose	ground	salmon

Q12   Write the **plurals** of the words below next to the correct **heading**:

wife	sandwich	officer	evidence
witness	continent	knife	thief
bench	life	series	camera

Add '**s**' in the plural: ....

Add '**es**' in the plural: ....

Change to '**ves**' in the plural: ....

Stay the **same** in the plural: ....

Prefixes

Q1   Circle the **prefixes** and underline the **root words** in these longer words.

    unknown   illogical   irregular   distaste   misspell

    incompetent   retrace   foretell   predate   midway

Q2   Rewrite these words with '**un-**' or '**in-**' to give the **opposite meaning**:

    a) important   ....   **e)** common   ....

    b) dependent   ....   **f)** conclusive   ....

    c) definite   ....   **g)** intentional   ....

    d) contested   ....   **h)** appropriate   ....

Q3   Add the prefixes '**il-**', '**im-**' or '**ir-**' to the root words below to complete the sentences:

    a) ......*legally* parked vehicles will be removed immediately.

    b) Some people thought women were too ......*rational* to have the vote.

    c) It's not always possible to explain the ......*regular* results of an experiment.

    d) ......*proper* use of the machinery could lead to injury.

    e) If you write ......*legibly* in your exam, you could lose some marks.

    f) Mrs Cox sent an ......*personal* letter to the head of the department.

    g) The mission's success is ......*refutable*.

    h) Many people in the 17th century were ......*literate*.

So, can anyone remember where we parked the van?

Q4   Add **prefixes** from the box to the root words below to create **two new** words.

    a) type   .... , ...

    b) view   .... , ...

    c) charge   .... , ...

    d) active   .... , ...

    e) trial   .... , ...

    f) arrange   .... , ...

    g) able   .... , ...

    h) count   .... , ...

mis-	over-
pre-	re-
dis-	un-
pro-	under-

Prefixes

Q5 Circle the **correct** word in italics to complete the sentences below correctly:

a) The Prime Minister asked for some *inpartial / impartial* advice.

b) Carla's reward was *disproportionate / misproportinate* to the effort she had made.

c) The protesters gave an *enpassioned / impassioned* response to the arrival of the police.

d) *Underloaded / Overloaded* vehicles can be serious road hazards.

e) The audience was *entranced / intranced* by the pianist's performance.

Q6 Add a **prefix** to each of the words in italics to complete the sentences below:

a) The players' bad behaviour brought the team into ....*repute*.

b) The returning soldiers were ....*whelmed* by the enthusiastic welcome they received.

c) Due to rising sea levels, low-lying islands like the Maldives will be ....*merged*.

d) The flood victims found the town's decision to proceed with the carnival ....*considerate*.

e) Some say the love between a parent and their child is ....*conditional*.

f) Personal items destroyed during an earthquake are often ....*replaceable*.

g) The trenches were particularly ....*pleasant* places to live.

h) Rewarding pupils for disrupting lessons would be an ....*conventional* approach.

i) The offensive poster was probably put up by people wishing to ....*credit* the King.

j) ....*ground* water and sewage pipes run beneath the building's foundations.

Q7 Some of the words have the **incorrect prefix** in the following passage.
Underline the mistakes and write the **correct words** in the box below.

Due to a silly disunderstanding, Mrs Dally accidentally rented out her property to the wrong tenant. She had intended to let Adam Richards live in the flat, but instead she discovered that a man called Richard Adams was moving in. Mrs Dally was nonsure as to how this had happened, but she suspected she'd been disled.

When she discussed the matter with her new tenant, he stared at her in disbelief and claimed she was speaking unsense. He said it was inpossible that such an error could have been made, and he was dishappy that she was questioning him in this rather unpolite manner.

Suffixes

Q1   Circle the **suffixes** and underline the **root words** in these longer words.

intended   waiter   camping   perfectly   motionless

questionable   amendment   inspector   thankful   dependence

Q2   Underline the **correct spellings** in italics to complete the sentences below:

a) During the *celebratetion / celebration*, balloons and sweets were handed out to visitors.

b) The council's decision to close the library upset the entire *community / communeity*.

c) The countries formed alliances for *security / secureity* reasons.

d) Some Christians believe that vocations are meant to be *challengeing / challenging*.

e) Hitler *persuaded / persuadeed* the Czech president to allow German troops into the country.

f) During a power cut, some businesses may rely on a back-up *generateor / generator*.

Q3   Add '**-able**' or '**-ible**' correctly to the words in italics:

a) The outbreak of war caused destruction on an *unimagin*.......... scale.

b) Our trip to the Arctic Circle was a truly *memor*.......... experience.

c) Staying in a youth hostel is a *sens*.......... way to save money on holiday.

d) You may be *inelig*.......... to sit on the board of directors.

e) The company believes bullying in the workplace is not *accept*...........

f) After the fire, officials declared the house *uninhabit*...........

g) You can make up statistics in an essay, but they must be *plaus*...........

Martin was able to get
into the veg box, but
getting out again was
going to be problematic...

Q4   Add a **suffix** from the box correctly to complete the words below:

-tion	-sion	-cian	-ssion

a) demonstra...............

b) deci...............

c) ten...............

d) politi...............

e) situa...............

f) interven...............

g) op...............

h) inva...............

i) oppre...............

j) segrega...............

k) discrimina...............

l) discu...............

m) opti...............

n) congrega...............

o) revi...............

p) confu...............

q) magi...............

r) emo...............

Suffixes

Q5 **Rewrite** these words, adding the **suffix** in brackets:

a) heavy *(er)* ....

b) lazy *(est)* ....

c) enjoy *(able)* ....

d) trendy *(est)* ....

e) dry *(ing)* ....

f) busy *(er)* ....

g) apply *(ing)* ....

h) hazy *(est)* ....

i) tricky *(er)* ....

j) weary *(ing)* ....

Q6 **Complete** the table below by correctly adding each **suffix** to the root words:

Root Word	-ing	-ful	-ed
hope			
care			
force			
doubt			
taste			
dread			
respect			

Q7 Add the **suffix** in brackets correctly to the **root words** in the sentences below:

a) Thousands of refugees left their homes in *desperate (tion)* ....·

b) Jesus challenged his followers' views about the *treat (ment)* .... of others.

c) Many countries were *response (ible)* .... for starting the war.

d) The Gospels are an important source of *guide (ance)* .... for Christians.

e) The country's problems should be handled with a sense of *urge (ency)* ....·

f) Roman Catholics believe in a state of *exist (ence)* .... called Purgatory.

g) Health *insure (ance)* .... pays for medical treatment.

h) There was a lot of *excite (ment)* .... about the company's new bonus scheme.

i) Juliet's actions show that she is *definite (ly)* .... not a submissive character.

Suffixes and Double Letters

Q1 Circle the **correct spellings** below:

a) equipped / equiped

c) forgotten / forgoten

e) masterrful / masterful

b) regretted / regreted

d) promotter / promoter

f) eventually / eventualy

Q2 Tick the words below which **double** their last letter when the suffix **'-ing'** is added.

signal ☐ intend ☐ prefer ☐ borrow ☐

visit ☐ offer ☐ admit ☐ consider ☐

refer ☐ listen ☐ happen ☐ budget ☐

whisper ☐ worship ☐ pretend ☐ accept ☐

Q3 **Complete** the table below by correctly adding each **suffix** to the root words:

Root Word	-ed	-ing	-ment
commit			
amend			
ship			
attain			
resent			
enrol			
develop			
fulfil			
recruit			

Suffixes and Double Letters

Q4 Add the **suffix** shown to each of the words in **brackets**.
Use the new word to **complete** the sentences below.

a) Denise claimed she was only a .... and that's why she lost. *(begin + er)*

b) The prince .... his right to become King of England. *(forfeit + ed)*

c) The government needs to start .... its budget. *(control + ing)*

d) The builders .... a proportion of the road to cyclists. *(allot + ed)*

e) Archeologists .... that the remains were not very old. *(admit + ed)*

f) Racism is a .... theme throughout the novel. *(recur + ing)*

Q5 Add the **suffix** in brackets correctly to the **root words** in the sentences below:

a) The German Mark became *virtual (ly)* .... *worth (less)* ....

b) The game between Spain and Wales turned out to be a *goal (less)* .... draw.

c) Investigators believed the facts had been *omit (ed)* .... from the report.

d) Each machine *gun (er)* .... was responsible for his or her own weapon.

e) In a mosque, women are not *permit (ed)* .... to lead the prayers of men.

f) The resistant rock is eroded more slowly and it's left *jut (ing)* .... out.

Q6 **Underline** the mistakes in the following sentences.
Write out the **correct spellings** on the dotted lines.

a) Rasheed accidentaly dropped the envelopes all over the floor. ....

b) Make sure your sketches are neat and clearly labeled. ....

c) The arguments continued, so the meeting was canceled. ....

d) The charity was commited to helping the environment. ....

e) Forgeting traumatic experiences can be a way of coping. ....

Q7 Write the words below next to the **correct** heading:

shrivel	catch	pedal	expel	proof	demand	protest	rebel

Double the last letter when adding 'ing': ....

....

Don't double the last letter when adding 'ing': ....

....

Other Words with Double Letters

Q1   Underline the words in italics that are **spelt correctly**:

a) Employees are paid for every *suggestion / sugestion* they make about productivity.

b) The Dr. Martin Luther King, Jr. *Association / Asocciation* is in San Jose, California.

c) Sam said his car cost over £50 000, but this was an *exagerration / exaggeration*.

d) Reducing our carbon footprint is considered to be absolutely *neccesary / necessary*.

e) Amanda and Erica were intimidated by the dog's *aggressive / agressive* behaviour.

f) The U-2 crisis caused *embarrassment / embarrasment* for President Eisenhower.

g) It was a momentous *ocasion / occasion* when America gained independence from Britain.

h) The fun run raised over £100 000, which proves the event was a huge *sucess / success*.

i) The *assassination / assasination* of Archduke Franz Ferdinand had devastating consequences.

j) Members of the tennis *comittee / committee* decided to resurface the tennis courts.

Q2   The words below are spelt **incorrectly**. Write the **correct** spellings on the dotted line.

dilema	bizare	disapoint	interupt
scisors	grashoper	recomend	tomorow

....

....

Q3   **Fill** the gaps in the words below with either a **single consonant** or a **double consonant**:

a) di......imilar

b) disa......ear

c) va......ish

d) di......erent

e) a......o......odation

f) be......onging

g) po......ession

h) addre......

i) co......unication

j) tra......ition

k) transmi......ing

l) co......unist

m) ther......ometer

n) o......ortunity

o) discri......inate

p) forbi......en

q) glo......al

r) emi......ion

Sid's got the hump. If he doubled it, he'd be twice as grumpy.

Silent Letters

Q1 Circle the **silent consonants** in the words below:

which   should   tsar   write   debt

scent   two   descend   wrong   kneel

gnome   while   would   womb   answer

Q2 Underline the words in italics that are **spelt correctly**:

a) Hayley isn't sure *wether / whether* to go for a walk — it *could / coud* start to rain.

b) Chalk is a *white / wite* sedimentary rock used to make concrete.

c) In the Bible, it states that Jesus had twelve *disiples / disciples*.

d) The *hole / whole* event was a disaster because *half / haf* of the bands didn't turn up.

e) Police had to cordon off the crime *sene / scene* to keep the public away.

Q3 **Underline** the mistakes in the following sentences.
Write out the **correct spellings** in the box underneath.

Tip: some sentences might have more than one mistake.

a) The defendant denied all nowledge of an attempt to overthrow the goverment.

b) Mrs Clark was annoyed that the children wouldn't lisen to her.

c) Historians don't kno wether the Knights of the Round Table existed or not.

d) Daniel finally told Ben the truth and was able to sleep with a clear consience.

e) I'm just going to the cemist to get some medication for my nee.

Q4 Solve the **clues** below to find the words that contain **silent letters**.

a) You might use a Bunsen burner in this lesson.   s............................

b) This is another word for a grave.   t............................

c) This building might have a moat and a drawbridge.   c............................

d) There's usually one of these for every question.   a............................

e) This religious festival celebrates the birth of Jesus.   C............................

Unstressed Vowels

Q1 Tick the words below which have an **unstressed 'a'** sound.

private ☐	happy ☐	alphabet ☐	woman ☐
man ☐	dictionary ☐	central ☐	challenge ☐
card ☐	separate ☐	maid ☐	trade ☐
original ☐	travel ☐	primary ☐	bedlam ☐

Q2 Circle the **correct spellings** of the words below:

a) different / diffurent

b) vegatable / vegetable

c) inturest / interest

d) marvellous / marvallous

e) general / genaral

f) originul / original

g) instrumant / instrument

h) necessary / necessery

i) totally / totelly

j) jewellary / jewellery

k) desperate / desparate

l) boundery / boundary

m) vowel / vowal

n) frighten / frighton

o) discribe / describe

Q3 Add a **letter** to complete the words in **italics** in these sentences.

a) The scientists can't explain the strange results — they're completely *rand....m*.

b) Our *postm....n* was unable to make the *deliv....ry* because he was scared of our dog.

c) There's a plaque in the town centre in *mem....ry* of fallen soldiers.

d) The USA wanted the treaty to be *gen....rous* to stop a similar war happening again.

e) Many people believe the *governm....nt* shouldn't dictate how charities spend their money.

f) Any outside *interfer....nce* will *defin....tely* have a *detriment....l* effect.

Q4 **Complete** the passage below by adding either 'a' or 'e':

The Darvaza Gas Crater in Turkmenistan is a curious *geographic....l* phenomenon in the

heart of the Karakum Desert. It is believed that the crater was created when a rig drilling for

natur....l gas *accident....lly* fell into an underground *cav....rn*. The *incid....nt* happened in 1971

and a fire has been burning in the crater ever since. The smell of burning sulphur can be detected

for quite some *dist....nce*.

i Before e Rule

Q1 Circle the words in the sentences below that are spelt **incorrectly**. Write the **correct** spellings in the box.

a) Even though my friend asked for a reciept for her dress, she didn't get one.

b) Although Jonathan is on a diet, he has just ordered a gigantic peice of cake.

c) When the phone rang, Caroline dashed to pick up the reciever.

d) It was a great releif to discover that the snake on my leg wasn't poisonous.

e) Whilst on holiday in the Arctic, my neighbour had to camp on a glaceir.

mine

Jonathan's

Q2 **Complete** the sentences below by adding either 'ei' or 'ie' to each word.

a) The *th......f* broke into the shop through the roof, making a hole in the *c......ling*.

b) Police officers tried to *s......ze* the armed robbers after a *f......rce* battle in the street.

c) If you *dec......ve* the judges, you will *forf......t* your right to stay in the competition.

d) During the *r......gn* of Queen Elizabeth I, many people had poor *hyg......ne*.

e) Pupils usually learn about *prot......ns* in *sc......nce* lessons.

f) Fishing boats can leak oil and *d......sel*, which harms aquatic animals.

g) Rocks can be changed by the pressure from the *w......ght* of the material above them.

h) *Sl......ghs* are sometimes used for transportation, especially in Arctic regions.

i) Pamela's *n......ce* is travelling to Australia next year.

j) When the alarm sounded, a *p......rcing* noise filled the air.

k) Food had to be rationed because there weren't *suffic......nt* supplies to feed the nation.

l) There are several *spec......s* of spider whose venom is poisonous to humans.

Q3 Add the **suffix** in brackets correctly to the **words** below:

a) agency (es) ....

b) heavy (er) ....

c) modify (ed) ....

d) vacancy (es) ....

e) fancy (ed) ....

f) deny (ed) ....

g) juicy (est) ....

h) clarify (ed) ....

Forming Comparatives

Q1 Tick the **sentences** below which form **comparatives correctly**.

a) Jupiter is bigger than Earth. ☐   Jupiter is more big than Earth. ☐

b) Sofas are comfortabler than stools. ☐   Sofas are more comfortable than stools. ☐

c) Health is importanter than money. ☐   Health is more important than money. ☐

d) I'm at greater risk than you are. ☐   I'm at more greater risk than you are. ☐

e) Japanese is harder than French. ☐   Japanese is more hard than French. ☐

Q2 Use the adjectives in **brackets** to form **comparatives** in these sentences:

a) Cycling to school is .... *(good)* than going by car.

b) The plague was .... *(bad)* than people expected.

c) Ruby has .... *(little)* money than Margaret.

d) Farmer Bob owns .... *(much)* land than Farmer Ted.

Farmer Bob, also known as Mr January in this year's edition of 'Farmers and their Fields'.

Q3 Use the adjectives in **brackets** and '**than**' to form **comparatives** in the sentences below:

a) Africa is .... Europe. *(large)*

b) Fruit and vegetables are .... fried food. *(healthy)*

c) Lakes are .... oceans. *(small)*

d) Steel is .... plastic. *(strong)*

e) Some countries are .... other countries. *(wealthy)*

f) Comics are usually .... magazines. *(funny)*

Q4 Use '**less... than**' and a suitable **adjective** from the **box** to fill in the gaps in these sentences:

challenging	stressful	successful	valuable	secure

Only use each word once.

a) Runners-up are .... winners.

b) Holidays are .... trips to the dentist.

c) Chipped antiques are .... antiques in perfect condition.

d) Flimsy bike locks are .... heavy-duty padlocks.

e) Easy questions are .... hard questions.

Forming Comparatives

Q5   Use 'as... as' and the word in **brackets** to fill the gaps in the sentences below:

    a) Melanie walks .... a snail. *(slowly)*

    b) In summer, our greenhouse feels .... an oven. *(hot)*

    c) King Richard I was .... a lion. *(brave)*

Q6   **Rewrite** the sentences below so that the **superlatives** are used **correctly**.

    a) Mount Everest is the most high mountain in the world.

    ....

    b) World War I was one of the most bad wars in history.

    ....

    c) Exam questions are the goodest way to practise what you've learnt.

    ....

    d) Liam gave the complicatedest answer possible.

    ....

Q7   Change the words below into **superlatives**. You will either need to use '**most**' or add '**est**'.

    a) clever   ....   **f)** fast   ....

    b) difficult   ....   **g)** famous   ....

    c) trendy   ....   **h)** original   ....

    d) confusing   ....   **i)** happy   ....

    e) deep   ....   **j)** dangerous   ....

Q8   Finish off these sentences with the **superlatives** of the underlined **adjectives**.

    a) Ron is <u>friendly</u>, but Jim is .... person I know.

    b) Geoff's house is <u>expensive</u>, but Julian's is .... house on the street.

    c) Cereal is <u>healthy</u>, but fruit is .... breakfast.

    d) Hobbies are <u>important</u>, but education is .... thing.

    e) Zoos are <u>fun</u>, but theme parks are ....

    f) Granny is <u>old</u>, but Great-Granny is .... relative I have.

    g) Claire's hair is <u>long</u>, but Tara's hair is .... hair I've ever seen.

Commonly Misused Words

Q1   Add '**maybe**' or '**may be**' correctly to the sentences below:

    a) Winston Churchill .... the most famous British Prime Minister in history.

    b) Carbon dioxide emissions .... harming the Earth's atmosphere.

    c) .... we should sail to France rather than go by plane.

    d) Christianity .... the fastest-growing religion in the world.

    e) The President's policy of high taxes was .... making the situation worse.

Q2   Circle the **correct option** from each of the words in italics.

    a) Some nations aim to help war-stricken countries in *anyway / any way* they can.

    b) *Everybody / Every body* of experts agreed on the report's findings.

    c) *No body / Nobody* can leave the room until *everyone / every one* of those windows is closed.

    d) Is *anybody / any body* interested in going on a trip to Prestatyn?

    e) The flood victims had enough support, but aid workers arrived on the scene *anyway / any way*.

    f) *Everybody / every body* who feels ill needs to go to see the nurse immediately.

    g) Life and death issues are important to *everyone / every one*.

    h) *Anybody / Any body* of deep water can be dangerous.

Q3   Use one of the words from the **box** to fill in the gaps in these sentences **correctly**:   *Only use each word once.*

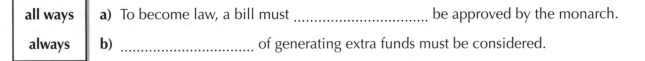

| all ways | **a)** To become law, a bill must .... be approved by the monarch. |
| always | **b)** .... of generating extra funds must be considered. |

| altogether | **c)** ...., King Henry VIII had six wives. |
| all together | **d)** If we approach the boss ...., maybe she'll listen to us. |

Q4   Add '**into**' or '**in to**' correctly to the sentences below:

    a) The toaster turned .... a robot.

    b) We went .... ask for directions.

    c) I handed my homework .... Mrs Watt.

    d) He had to stay .... do the chores.

    e) The dog sneaked .... the hairdressers.

Short back and sides, please, Julie.

Commonly Misused Words

Q5   Use the letters 's' and 'c' to fill in the gaps **correctly** in the following sentences:

a) Some Catholics *practi....e* their religion by attending Mass on a regular basis.

b) If you want to renew your *licen....e*, you'll have to take the test again.

c) The Prime Minister's aide was unable to give any practical *advi....e*.

d) It would be great if there was a *devi....e* for controlling the weather.

e) Martin Luther King *advi....ed* people to never lose hope.

Tip: first work out whether the word is a verb or a noun.

f) Vanessa is *licen....ed* to drive heavy goods vehicles.

g) Many religious *practi....es* were banned in the Soviet Union.

h) We need to *devi....e* a cunning plan to outsmart the enemy.

Q6   Circle the **correct option** from each of the words in italics.

a) Parliament *passed / past* the Abolition of Death Penalty Act in 1965.

b) The *effects / affects* of the Hiroshima and Nagasaki bombings can still be seen today.

c) The speeding driver had to *except / accept* the consequences of his actions.

d) Cliffs formed from soft rock or *lose / loose* material can retreat quickly.

e) The River Rhine runs *passed / past* Cologne, Bonn and Koblenz.

f) All the inventions, *accept / except* the chocolate teapot, were awarded a prize.

g) If shareholders *lose / loose* confidence, they may sell their shares.

h) Evacuation *effected / affected* thousands of children during the war.

Q7   Circle the **mistakes** in the letter below and write the **correct** spellings on the dotted line.

Dear Gareth,

   Thankyou so much for the wonderful birthday present. It's the best gift I've received in a long time. Infact, I would go so far as to say it's the best present I've ever been given. It would be great to hear from you soon — I've enclosed a note with my address on it incase you've forgotten it.

   Once again, thanks alot.

   Michael

....

Write down what the mistakes above have **in common** on the dotted line below.

....

Commonly Misused Words

Q8   Add 'there', 'their' or 'they're' correctly to the passage below:

.... are many reasons why people decide to change .... religion. Some

people choose to convert due to a change in .... beliefs. Others might be forced to

follow a different faith by a totalitarian regime controlling .... country. In this case,

citizens might feel as though .... putting .... lives at risk if they don't agree to

convert to a new religion.

Q9   Use a word from the **box** to fill in the gaps in these sentences **correctly**:

Only use each word once.

where	were	wear

a) Soldiers usually .... camouflaged uniforms so they blend in with their environment.

b) If we take a compass, we should be able to work out .... we are.

c) When we finally arrived at the summit, we .... ready for a long rest.

Q10   Add 'to', 'two' and 'too' correctly to the sentences below:

a) After the war, the main powers found they had spent .... much money on the war.

b) The next planned mission .... Mars has been postponed until further notice.

c) Plates are made of .... types of crust — continental and oceanic.

d) If someone embraces Islam later in life, he or she is said .... be 'returning'.

e) Although deforestation has some positive impacts, it has quite a lot of negative ones ....

Q11   Add 'off' or 'of' correctly to the sentences below:

a) The field .... science is fascinating and complex.

b) During air raids, street lights were switched ....

c) Oceans cover roughly 71 per cent .... the Earth's surface.

d) The shoe shop's sale sign says, "All boots 80% ....".

80% of Dea's boot was filled with dogs, not bargain boots.

Q12   Circle the **correct option** from each of the words in italics.

a) Judaism teaches that we should look after those who *our / are* less fortunate than ourselves.

b) Fair elections and the right to peaceful protest *our / are* vital parts of *our / are* society.

c) Some people believe *our / are* existence is a test to see if we *our / are* fit for Heaven.

Commonly Misused Words

Q13 Use a word from the **box** to fill in the gaps in these sentences **correctly**:

though	thought	through	thorough

a) .... the 1920s had been a 'boom time', there were economic problems.

b) If you present a .... analysis of the facts, you'll do well in the exam.

c) The German troops went .... Belgium to attack France.

d) The Prime Minister raised taxes even .... it was unpopular.

e) In the 17ᵗʰ century, many people .... that the Earth was flat.

f) The .... reshuffling of the cabinet caused some ministers to lose their jobs.

g) Tunnels have been drilled .... some fold mountains to make straight roads.

h) The report was a .... investigation into the business's problems.

i) Magma rises .... cracks in the Earth's crust.

j) For many believers, Heaven is a comforting ....

Q14 Circle the **correct option** from each of the words in italics.

a) Some citizens were worried that joining the League of Nations could cost *those / them* money.

b) Jairus was a synagogue ruler whose daughter was *bought / brought* back to life by Jesus.

c) The Cuban Missile Crisis of 1962 *bought / brought* the world to the brink of nuclear war.

d) The aid may not reach *those / them* who need it because of things like transport problems.

e) People had to use rationing coupons when they *bought / brought* butter, sugar and meat.

f) Indoctrinating pupils was aimed to make *those / them* less likely to resist Nazi control.

g) The reward for *those / them* who have followed Allah will be entry into Paradise.

h) High order goods, such as washing machines, are only *bought / brought* occasionally.

i) King Duncan is praised for rewarding *them / those* who are loyal to him.

Q15 Use one of the words from the **box** to fill in the gaps in these sentences **correctly**:   *Only use each word once.*

teach
learn

a) Training schemes help people to .... new skills.

b) Most religions .... that we all move on to an afterlife.

lend
borrow

c) The Dawes Plan meant the US would .... money to Germany.

d) Very poor countries .... money from other countries.

Other Tricky Words

Q1 Correct the **spelling** of the following words:

a) reccomend ....

b) temperary ....

c) definately ....

d) unfortunitely ....

e) analise ....

f) relevent ....

g) probibly ....

h) sucess ....

i) seperate ....

j) opinien ....

k) referance ....

l) interoting ....

Q2 Add a **letter** to complete the words in **italics** in these sentences.

a) The first part of President Truman's speech was a strong *criti...ism* of Communism.

b) Cardinals are *respons...ble* for electing the Pope's successor.

c) People from rural areas sometimes *bel...eve* that the standard of living is better in cities.

d) The photo aimed to *pers...ade* German people that Hitler was a good leader.

e) Criminals who commit crimes in the heat of the moment don't think about the *conse...uences*.

f) The source has been written to *exa...gerate* the importance of Stalin.

Q3 Some of the words are spelt **incorrectly** in the following sentences.
Underline the mistakes and write the **correct words** in the box below.

a) The negative impacts of tourism may not be immediately apparant.

b) Headlands are usually made of resistant rocks that have weakneses like cracks.

c) Governments deside how taxes are spent, and how much is collected.

d) There are many arguements both for and against the abolition of capital punishment.

e) Once the farmers have been taught the new tecnique, they'll be able to carry on using it.

f) The country voted in favour of indapendence.

g) The close contour lines on the map are evidence of a waterfall.

h) The army was poorly organised; many officers were inexperienced and disipline was poor.

i) Jews believe that God's inteligance is vastly higher than ours.

Other Tricky Words

Q4   Circle the **correct option** from each of the groups below:

a) successful / sucessful   g) strenth / strength

b) becase / because   h) schedule / scedule

c) similer / similar   i) leisure / lesure

d) necessary / neccesary   j) libary / library

e) expirience / experience   k) ocurrence / occurrence

f) basically / basicaly   l) rhyme / ryhme

Well, I do a great Darth Vader impression.

Q5   The words below are spelt **incorrectly**. Write the **correct** spellings on the dotted lines.

a) remeber   ....   f) aquire   ....

b) permanant ....   g) equiptment ....

c) conclution ....   h) medival ....

d) foregn   ....   i) relevent ....

e) gard   ....   j) vacum   ....

Q6   **Rewrite** the sentences below so that they are **correct**.

a) Bus prioraty lanes speed up bus services.

....

b) Quakers are particulerly likely to oppose hunting.

....

c) Romeo kills Tybalt and is conseqently banished.

....

d) Plans for developement will generate more jobs.

....

e) Cheating in exams is not acceptible.

....

Q7   Circle the **correct option** from each of the words in italics.

a) Mother Teresa won the Nobel *Peace / Piece* Prize in 1979.

b) Weak earthquakes happen *quiet / quite* often, but strong earthquakes are rare.

c) Vehicles can cause pollution even when they are *stationary / stationery*.

Mixed Practice

Q1   Complete the sentences below using the correct **plural form** of the word in brackets.

   a) Some Christians reject scientific .... *(theory)* on evolution.

   b) Glaciers are masses of ice that fill .... *(valley)*.

   c) Some people believe that .... *(miracle)* in religious texts are metaphors.

   d) The Five Pillars of Islam provide .... *(opportunity)* to know Allah.

   e) The priest gave a short sermon about Christian .... *(belief)*.

   f) For .... *(century)*, the finest work of leading artists was made for churches.

   g) .... *(volcano)* are a source of geothermal energy.

   h) .... *(sheep)* and goats are sacrificed at the Eid ul-Adha festival.

   i) A severe flood could make entire .... *(community)* homeless.

Q2   Add a **prefix** to each of the words below to give their **opposite meaning**.

Word	Opposite
usual	
consistency	
legal	
counted	

Word	Opposite
confident	
sustainable	
rational	
understood	

Q3   Underline the **correct spellings** in italics to complete the sentences below:

   a) The conductor stands at the front of the orchestra, facing the *musicians / musisions*.

   b) Stalin controlled all information *availible / available* to the Russian people.

   c) In a river, the *heaviest / heavyest* material is deposited closest to the river channel.

   d) Traffic congestion and *pollusion / pollution* are higher in cities.

   e) The American Dream made people think that anyone could be *successfull / successful*.

   f) In the Bible, Job endures *terrible / terrable* suffering and he questions God.

   g) Sceptics argue that religious experiences are just *illutions / illusions*.

   h) Some countries couldn't understand why nobody stood up to Hitler *earlier / earlyer*.

Mixed Practice

Q4 Add the **suffixes '-ed'** and **'-ing'** correctly to each word below.

a) travel .... , ...   f) trap .... , ...

b) pump .... , ...   g) dip .... , ...

c) benefit .... , ...   h) nod .... , ...

d) cancel .... , ...   i) offer .... , ...

e) prefer .... , ...   j) tap .... , ...

Q5 Circle the words below that are spelt **incorrectly**, and write the **correct** spelling in the box.

revolution   yestarday   recesion   freedem

aceleration   heaven   doubt

secretery   communism   biscit   ceramony

Q6 Add '**ei**' or '**ie**' to **complete** the words in the sentences below:

a) The farmer tried to keep the cows in *th......r f......ld.*

b) I *bel......ve* the *ch......f* problem in our *soc......ty* is homelessness.

c) There are several *agenc......s* that help people to lose *w......ght.*

d) *Dec......t* is a prominent theme in Shakespeare's 'Macbeth'.

e) The *juic......st* oranges come from Spain.

f) *N......ther* side was willing to admit defeat.

Come on, chaps.
Let's go. The grass is
greener over there...

Q7 Fill the gaps in these sentences with a **comparative**, using the word in brackets and either '**than**' or '**more...than**'.

a) Jonah was .... Paul when pay cuts were announced. *(upset)*

b) Bulk buying can be .... making individual purchases. *(cheap)*

c) A sand beach is .... a shingle beach. *(flat)*

d) The first candidates were .... the second lot of candidates. *(positive)*

e) Broadsheet newspapers are usually .... the tabloid press. *(serious)*

f) Winter evenings are .... summer evenings. *(dark)*

Mixed Practice

Q8 Change the words below into **superlatives**.

Tip: for most words, add either 'most' or '-est'.

a) regular ....

b) late ....

c) creative ....

d) close ....

e) less ....

f) popular ....

g) painful ....

h) terrible ....

i) lucky ....

j) friendly ....

Q9 Underline the **correct spellings** in italics to complete the sentences below:

a) Businesses *maybe / may be* set up to cater for the tourists, e.g. souvenir shops or hotels.

b) Voting is secret so no one can be pressured *into / in to* voting for one particular candidate.

c) The politicians couldn't see *anyway / any way* of getting the bill through Parliament.

d) Not *everybody / every body* has access to services like healthcare and education.

e) Winds *all ways / always* blow from areas of high pressure to areas of low pressure.

f) Most drugs *affect / effect* people's judgement, so they are more likely to take risks.

g) Businesses can be damaged by floods, so people can *lose / loose* their income.

h) It's difficult to say that *anyone / any one* reason is the main reason for Hitler's rise.

i) In 1975, the Sex Discrimination Act was *past / passed* by Parliament.

Q10 **Rewrite** the sentences below, changing any words that are **wrong** and correcting any **misspellings**.

a) Mercutio curses the too feuding families.

....

b) During worship, Jewish men often were special clothing.

....

c) Christians try to help them who need it.

....

d) King Duncan's sons fear for there lives.

....

e) Parents may learn their children to show forgiveness.

....

f) Romeo hates the though off living without Juliet.

....

Mixed Practice

Q11 Circle the words below that are spelt **incorrectly**, and write the **correct** spelling in the box.

acomodate   bizarre   whereever   tommorow

religious   liaise   collegue

across   completly   pavillion   environment

Q12 **Complete** the spelling of the word in **italics** in the sentences below.

a) Elected *commi......ees* of workers, peasants and soldiers were set up in 1905.

b) Military *perso......el* entered the village to support the civilians.

c) Squatter settlements often govern themselves more *su......essfully* than you might expect.

d) Life was *begi......ing* to look better for Germany thanks to the work of Stresemann.

e) In the exam, use specialist vocabulary where *a......ropriate*.

f) A war may be considered just if it frees people from *tyra......y*.

g) Preparation doesn't *guarant......* safety from a flood.

Q13 Draw lines to **match** up each **word beginning** with the correct **ending**:

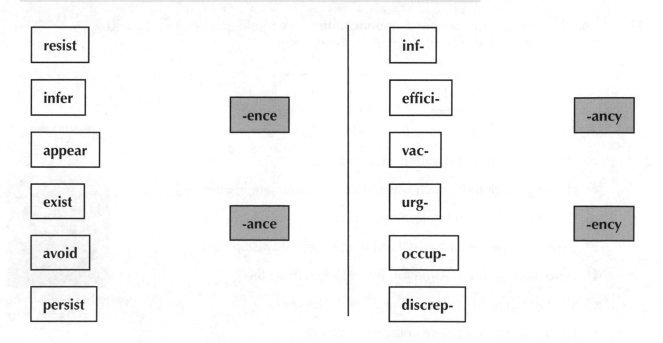

resist	inf-
infer	effici-
appear	vac-
exist	urg-
avoid	occup-
persist	discrep-

-ence   -ance   -ancy   -ency

Section Two — Punctuation

Sentence Punctuation

Q1   **Tick** the sentences that use **capital letters** correctly.

a) Canberra, not Sydney, is the Capital of Australia. ☐

b) In February, there is often heavy snowfall in the Alps. ☐

c) By April 1932, conditions in Germany were very difficult. ☐

d) For catholics, the virgin Mary is an important figure. ☐

e) The treaty of Versailles caused resentment among germans. ☐

Q2   **Rewrite** these sentences to include **capital letters** where necessary.

a) the european union has introduced new laws.

....

b) england used to be ruled by a danish king.

....

c) meera syal wrote 'anita and me'.

....

d) christians celebrate easter and christmas.

....

e) lenin fled to finland after the bolsheviks were defeated.

....

Q3   Add the most appropriate form of **punctuation** to complete the sentences below. You may use each punctuation mark more than once.

!	?	.

a) The American stock market crashed in 1929 ......

b) Did women have the right to vote in 1930 ......

c) He was wondering which was the highest mountain in Europe ......

d) Lady Macbeth is an interesting character ......

e) I loved the performance of 'Lord of the Flies'; it was brilliant ......

f) Who did the Nazis blame for the 1933 Reichstag fire ......

g) She ran out of her last exam and cried, "It's over ......"

h) Destructive waves cause coastlines to erode ......

*Mike had always believed he was
Lord of the Fly Fishing.*

Sentence Punctuation

Q4 **Circle** the **correct option** for each of these sentences.

a) Honduras was badly affected by *Hurricane / hurricane* Mitch in 1998.

b) Victor Frankenstein is a *Scientist / scientist* with an obsessive desire for knowledge.

c) General Nivelle was a French officer during *World war one / World War One*.

d) Russia was ruled by *Tsars / tsars* until Nicholas II abdicated.

e) The *League of Nations / league of nations* was the idea of Woodrow Wilson.

f) Many Christians go to church on *Sundays / sundays*.

g) There are often endangered species in *national parks / National Parks*.

Q5 **Rewrite** the passage below so that the **capital letters** and **sentence endings** are correct. There are **ten** mistakes.

England is a Country which has clear seasons. Winter, which runs from December to February, has colder temperatures and fewer hours of daylight. There may even be snow during winter in England? In contrast, the Summer months (june to august) see higher temperatures and longer hours of daylight.

Cambodia has very different seasons to England. The temperatures throughout the year remain high, and hours of daylight are mostly constant. Instead, Cambodia has clear Wet and Dry Seasons. November to April are relatively dry, while Monsoons from May to October bring high rainfall!

Commas

Q1   Add **commas** in the correct places in the sentences below.

   a) Edward Rochester Mrs Reed Helen Burns and Blanche Ingram
   are four of the characters in 'Jane Eyre'.

   b) India China Thailand and Pakistan are all situated in Asia.

   c) Sedimentary igneous and metamorphic are the three types of rock.

   d) The Treaty of Versailles was signed by Germany France Britain and the USA.

   e) Victor brings a destructive menacing creature to life.

   f) Women still worked in low-skilled low-paid jobs in the 1920s.

   g) Macbeth is a brave ambitious soldier.

Q2   **Combine** each pair of sentences using a **comma** and the **connective** in brackets.

   a) Mussolini ruled Italy. *(but)* He was overthrown in 1943.

   ....

   b) Read the source. *(and)* Think about the facts you know.

   ....

   c) Some Christians pray to saints. *(but)* Not all do.

   ....

   d) Magwitch is a criminal. *(yet)* Pip feels sorry for him.

   ....

Q3   **Put** a **cross** next to the sentences which should
   use a **comma** and **write** them out **correctly** below.

   a) He wore light blue jeans.   ☐

   b) They watched a long boring film.   ☐

   c) It was a dark rainy day.   ☐

   d) The bright yellow bike is mine.   ☐

   e) It was a cold calculated decision. ☐

Tip: if you can separate the adjectives with 'and', you should use a comma.

   ....

   ....

   ....

Commas

Q4 Add **commas** in the sentences below so they separate **extra information**.

a) The Torah the Jewish holy book gives followers advice about how to live.

b) Winston Churchill a British Prime Minister was succeeded by Clement Attlee.

c) Mallorca one of the Spanish Balearic islands is a popular tourist destination.

d) Catholicism a denomination of Christianity does not permit divorce.

e) In Russia, the Kulaks richer peasants were resented for their wealth.

f) The Rhône Glacier situated in the Swiss Alps is about 7.8 km long.

Q5 **Rewrite** the sentences, using **commas** to add in the **extra information** shown in brackets.

a) Benvolio tries to cheer Romeo up. (Romeo's cousin)

....

b) Trevor Huddleston campaigned against apartheid. (an English bishop)

....

c) The Suez Canal runs through Egypt. (an important trade route)

....

d) Deforestation leads to soil erosion. (the removal of trees)

....

e) 'Animal Farm' was published in 1945. (a short novel)

....

Q6 Add **commas** in the correct places in the sentences below.

a) Although earthly life is short Muslims still believe it is very important.

b) While the men were at war women had to take on jobs at home.

c) After the book was published the author became famous.

d) Although the Allies won World War One there was little celebration.

e) Before you write an essay you need to write a rough plan.

f) When a river floods onto a flood plain the water slows down.

g) If you have time go back and check your work.

h) Since God is invisible Jews use symbols to help them focus on God in private prayer and in communal worship.

Comma, comma, comma, comma, comma-chameleon...

Commas

Q7 Put a **tick** in the box next to the sentences that use commas **correctly** and a **cross** in the boxes next to the sentences that use commas **incorrectly**.

a) Lydia the youngest Bennet sister elopes with George Wickham. ☐

b) In earthquake-prone areas, people take part in earthquake drills. ☐

c) Islam Christianity and Judaism all teach that there is only one god. ☐

d) Granite areas are good for quarrying, tourism, rearing livestock and building reservoirs. ☐

e) As the novel progresses the boys descend into savagery. ☐

f) In Exmoor National Park, strategies are needed to cope with the impact of tourism. ☐

Now **write out** the incorrect sentences, putting **commas** in the **correct places**.

....

....

....

....

Q8 Write in the **five missing commas** in the passage below.

'Romeo and Juliet' is a play about love fate and conflict. It's set in the Italian city of Verona, and it tells the story of two young lovers.

At the start of the play, the Capulet and Montague families are engaged in a bitter bloody conflict. When Romeo and Juliet who are members of the warring families fall in love, they know that it will be difficult for them to be together.

Friar Laurence agrees to help them marry arranging for Juliet to fake her own death. This would allow her to run away with Romeo. However, his plan goes tragically wrong, and both lovers die needlessly at the end of the play.

Q9 **Write out** the passage below, with **commas** in the correct places.

After World War One Britain France and the USA made Germany sign a treaty. The treaty which imposed harsh punishments was unpopular in Germany.

....

....

....

Colons

Q1 Add **colons** to introduce **lists** in the sentences below.

a) There are many examples of religious charities Christian Aid, Islamic Relief, Tearfund, World Jewish Relief and CAFOD.

b) The hydrological cycle has three parts the sea, the land and the atmosphere.

c) Miss Havisham can be described in two words eccentric and hateful.

d) America had several allies during the Second World War Britain, France, China, New Zealand, Australia, Canada and the Soviet Union.

e) There are five Bennet sisters Jane, Elizabeth, Mary, Kitty and Lydia.

f) The 20th century saw the rise of numerous European dictators Hitler, Mussolini, Franco and several others.

g) World War Two brought several new policies evacuation, rationing and censorship.

h) These are the key themes in 'Romeo and Juliet' love, conflict and fate.

i) Droughts have several secondary impacts soil erosion, food shortages, unemployment and wildfires.

Q2 Put a **tick** in the box next to the sentences that use colons **correctly** and a **cross** in the boxes next to the sentences that use colons **incorrectly**.

a) The army suffered heavy losses in the war: 10 000 troops died. ☐

b) Fold mountains are good places to build ski resorts: they have steep slopes. ☐

c) Granite is: impermeable it does not let water through. ☐

d) The play is a tragedy it ends with: the protagonist's downfall. ☐

e) Christianity values marriage: it reflects the union of Jesus with his followers. ☐

f) Hydraulic action is a process of erosion: water breaks down rock particles. ☐

g) Darcy rejects Elizabeth he says that: she is not pretty enough. ☐

h) Christians believe God can do anything: he is all-powerful. ☐

i) Fred is the opposite of Scrooge he is cheerful: and optimistic. ☐

Now **write out** the incorrect sentences, putting **colons** in the **correct places**.

....

....

....

....

....

Semicolons

Q1 Put a **tick** in the box next to the sentences that use semicolons **correctly** and a **cross** in the boxes next to the sentences that use semicolons **incorrectly**.

a) Romeo is from the Montague; family Juliet is a Capulet. ☐

b) Flow lines on a map show movement desire lines show; a journey. ☐

c) East Berlin was communist; West Berlin was democratic. ☐

d) Atheists believe there is no god agnostics believe; it is impossible to know if God exists. ☐

e) The map shows motorways, marked in blue; main roads, marked in red; secondary roads, marked in orange; and minor roads, marked in yellow. ☐

Q2 Add **semicolons** in the correct places in the sentences below.

a) Christians believe in Heaven and Hell Jews believe in Gan Eden and Gehinnom.

b) Muslim parents often arrange marriages for their children they also have a responsibility to help out if the marriage begins to go wrong.

c) Climate change will affect the crops that farmers are able to grow certain habitats may also be destroyed.

d) Planning your essay means that you can organise your ideas leaving time to read over your work gives you the chance to spot silly errors.

e) Shield volcanoes have runny lava dome volcanoes have thicker lava.

f) The British lost 14 ships in the battle the Germans lost 11 ships.

Q3 Add **semicolons** in the correct places in the sentences below to break up the lists of long phrases. Each sentence will need more than one semicolon.

a) Important Jewish festivals include Yom Kippur, which takes place ten days after Jewish New Year Pesach, or Passover, which commemorates the night of the Exodus from Egypt and Hanukkah, which celebrates the story of a day's worth of oil burning for eight days during the rededication ceremony for the Temple in Jerusalem.

b) There are several different types of nouns: proper nouns, which are the names of particular people, places or things common nouns, which name kinds of things collective nouns, which name groups of things and abstract nouns, which name ideas.

c) The USA failed to defeat the communists in South Vietnam for several reasons: the American troops, most of whom were very young, were not used to fighting in the jungle the Vietcong, the South Vietnamese communist soldiers, were very skilled in guerilla warfare and public support for the war in the USA was decreasing.

d) Weather conditions can be tested using a thermometer to measure the temperature a barometer to measure the air pressure, and whether it's rising or falling a wind vane to determine the direction the wind is blowing and an anemometer to measure the wind speed.

Colons and Semicolons

Q1 Choose between **colons** and **semicolons** to complete the following sentences.

a) In 1900, there were five main rival nations in Europe .... Britain, France, Russia, Austria-Hungary and Germany.

b) Shakespeare emphasises the status of some characters through their language .... they speak in verse.

c) Christians believe in the idea of stewardship .... the responsibility of humans to look after God's creation.

d) There are different types of ecosystems in the world, such as the hot, dry deserts .... the hot, wet tropical rainforests .... and the mild, wet climates where temperate deciduous forests are found.

Meg knew she was a cool cat; she loved her new fake fur coat.

e) There are several themes in 'Animal Farm' .... power, language, class and education.

f) Stalin died in 1953 .... he'd been the USSR's leader since the 1920s.

g) Jews worship in a synagogue .... Muslims worship in a mosque.

Q2 Some of these sentences use **colons** and **semicolons** incorrectly. **Rewrite** these sentences with the **correct punctuation**. If the sentence is correct, just put a **tick** on the dotted line.

a) Jews practise Tzedakah the donation of 10%: of their wealth to the poorest in society.

....

....

b) Earthquakes can have secondary impacts water shortages: gas leaks and landslides.

....

....

c) The novel has several main characters; Ralph, the boys' elected leader: Jack, who rebels against Ralph: Piggy, an overweight, intelligent outsider: and Simon, who is kind, shy and spiritual.

....

....

....

....

d) The play is set in 1912; Priestly wanted to expose the inequalities in society at the time.

....

....

Brackets

Q1   Add a pair of **brackets** to each of the sentences below.

a) Christians believe that God sacrificed Jesus his son to forgive the sins of mankind .

b) The Inspector announces the death of Arthur's ex-employee Eva Smith in Act One .

c) In 1923, France invaded and occupied an industrial region of Germany the Ruhr .

d) In Antarctica, summer December-February temperatures are generally close to freezing .

e) Most Hindus worship at home, but some also visit a mandir Hindu temple .

f) Mussolini head of the Italian Fascist Party became Prime Minister in 1922 .

g) The average summer temperature in the UK about 14°C is lower than mainland Europe .

h) In 'Great Expectations', Magwitch a convict is revealed as Pip's secret benefactor .

Q2   **Rewrite** each of the sentences below to include a pair of **brackets**.

a) Islam is a monotheistic religion followers only believe in one god.

....

b) The Berlin Wall built in 1961 divided Germany in two.

....

c) Received pronunciation RP is a type of accent.

....

d) Supervolcanoes form over hotspots really hot areas of mantle.

....

e) 'Extensive' an adjective means 'thorough' or 'large'.

....

f) TNCs Trans-National Corporations create jobs in an area.

....

Q3   There are 3 pairs of **brackets missing** from the passage below.
Write in the **brackets** in the correct places.

World War One was fought between the Triple Alliance Germany,
Austria-Hungary and Italy and the Triple Entente France, Britain and Russia .
Tensions between the two alliances exploded after the assassination of Archduke
Franz Ferdinand an Austro-Hungarian aristocrat by a Serbian in 1914 .

Hyphens

Q1   Circle the correct option in each of the following sentences.

a) When the February Revolution came, Lenin left Switzerland and *reentered / re-entered* Russia.

b) Many people show their desire for peace by attending *anti-war protests / anti war-protests*.

c) The Earth's mantle is made up of *semi molten / semi-molten* rock.

d) It's useful to *re-read / reread* a comprehension text before answering the questions.

e) The War Department created *anti-German propaganda / anti German-propaganda*.

f) The edge of a cliff can eventually *disappear / dis-appear* if the rock is heavily weathered.

g) Political parties are usually made up of *like minded / like-minded* people.

h) *Large scale / Large-scale* commercial farming contributes to deforestation in the Amazon.

Q2   Add the **prefix** in brackets to each of these words.

Tip: not every word needs a hyphen here.

a) *(semi)* interested   ....

b) *(re)* educate   ....

c) *(ex)* President   ....

d) *(pro)* communist   ....

e) *(un)* prepared   ....

f) *(anti)* Nazi   ....

g) *(under)* estimate   ....

h) *(self)* absorbed   ....

Jill was determined to get Jack to make the most of their all-inclusive deal.

Q3   Tick the correct **meaning** of each sentence or phrase in italics.

a) *I recovered a chair.*

I got the chair back. ☐   I put another cover on it. ☐

b) *He re-signed today.*

He left his job. ☐   He signed something again. ☐

c) *the little-known town*

The town is little but well-known. ☐   The town is not well-known. ☐

d) *the four year-old children*

four children that are a year old ☐   children that are four years old ☐

e) *the reformed parliament*

the improved parliament ☐   the parliament that had formed again ☐

Apostrophes and Missing Letters

Q1 Use **apostrophes** to make **shortened forms** of the words in italics. Write your answers on the dotted lines.

a) Victor and William are brothers: *they are* related. ....

b) *We are* all responsible for the environment. ....

c) Drivers *cannot* legally drive without a licence. ....

d) A good Muslim *should not* disobey Allah. ....

e) Ralph and Piggy *do not* want to join the hunters. ....

f) American troops *could not* defeat the Vietcong. ....

g) *I would* always recommend taking time to plan an essay. ....

h) Stalin exaggerated the role *he had* had in the Revolution. ....

i) Think about *who is* writing a source and why. ....

Q2 Use **apostrophes** to write shortened versions of the phrases below.

Long Word	Shortened Word
does not	
will not	
they have	
I am	

Long Word	Shortened Word
I have	
who would	
let us	
I had	

Q3 **Circle** the correct word to complete these sentences.

a) The Lake District is a national park *thats' / that's* home to deer and red squirrels.

b) The Cratchits *haven't / have'nt* got much money, but they love one another.

c) In Judaism, *there's / theres'* a strong emphasis on moral behaviour in this life.

d) Soldiers *whod' / who'd* survived the war were disillusioned when they returned home.

e) On the Sabbath, Jews *aren't / are'nt* supposed to do any work.

f) Without funds, the union *was'nt / wasn't* in a position to threaten new strikes.

g) Buildings can be strengthened so that *they're / theyr'e* more resistant to earthquakes.

Section Two — Punctuation

Apostrophes and Missing Letters

Q4   Add an **apostrophe** to the words in **italics** to complete these sentences.

   a) *Englands* bordered by Wales and Scotland.

   b) The Bible teaches that Christians *shouldnt* be selfish with their wealth.

   c) The USSR *couldnt* afford to keep building up its nuclear arsenal.

   d) Most people *dont* feel earthquakes of magnitude 1-2 on the Richter scale.

   e) Estella rejects Pip *whos* kind and loving towards her.

   f) *Tourisms* a growing industry — people are having more, longer holidays.

   g) *Theres* a destructive plate margin along the coast of Indonesia.

Q5   **Circle** the **mistakes** in the following sentences. **Write** out the sentences **correctly** underneath.

   a) Britain couldnt' send supplies by sea to its troops' abroad.

   ....

   b) Soil erosion happen's when theres heavy rainfall.

   ....

   c) Buildings can be put on stilt's so theyre safe from floods.

   ....

   d) Mr Darcy doesnt let Miss Bingley's compliments affect him.

   ....

   e) Photo's can be useful sources when youre studying the past.

   ....

   f) The boy's are convinced that theres a beast on the island.

   ....

Q6   Write either **lets** or **let's** in the gap for the following sentences.

   a) Some Christians believe that contraception .... parents plan their family responsibly.

   b) We can learn a lot from our past, so .... study the causes of World War One.

   c) .... discuss the use of symbolism in the play.

   d) Work experience .... you find out what a job is like.

   e) Renewable energy .... areas develop in a more sustainable way.

Possessive Apostrophes

Q1 Use **possessive apostrophes** and add an 's' to shorten the phrases below.

a) the wealth of the country .... the country's wealth ....

b) the cane belonging to Hyde ....

c) the invention belonging to Victor ....

d) the borders of France ....

e) the beliefs of a Hindu ....

f) the son of Mrs Lyons ....

g) the wildlife of an area ....

h) the wedding vows of the couple ....

Q2 Add **apostrophes** in the correct places to complete these sentences.

a) Regular prayer keeps Allah in a Muslims mind.

b) The worlds longest river is the Nile.

c) The countrys capital is New Delhi.

d) A rivers depth is affected by rainfall.

e) The regions main industry is tourism.

f) The characters childhood is troubled and lonely.

g) By 1933, 83% of the US stock markets value had been lost.

h) The womens aim was to have the same voting rights as men.

i) A religions teachings can be interpreted in different ways.

j) The novels characters are often ignorant or prejudiced.

Nigel didn't need an apostrophe to know the shot put trophy was his.

Q3 **Draw lines** to show whether there is **one** or **more than one** of the underlined noun.

a) The <u>mountains'</u> slopes were steep.

b) He cleaned the <u>horse's</u> hooves.

c) The <u>animals'</u> lives changed.

d) The government spent the <u>taxpayers'</u> money.

e) The <u>soldiers'</u> bags were heavy.

f) The <u>town's</u> plans were approved.

g) The <u>minister's</u> decision was criticised.

h) The <u>river's</u> banks burst.

i) The <u>boys'</u> behaviour becomes more savage.

one

more than one

Possessive Apostrophes

Q4   Use **possessive apostrophes** and add an 's' to shorten the phrases below.

a) the house belonging to the Johnstones ⟹ the .... house

b) the struggle belonging to the workers ⟹ the .... struggle

c) the protests belonging to the women ⟹ the .... protests

d) the cheese belonging to the mice ⟹ the .... cheese

e) the adventure belonging to the girls ⟹ the .... adventure

f) the books belonging to the children ⟹ the .... books

Q5   Add the word in the box and an **apostrophe** or an **apostrophe** and 's' to complete the sentences correctly.

rainforest   The .... ecosystem is very fragile.

sisters   The .... mother is a seamstress.

countries   The war went against the .... agreement.

suffragettes   Newspapers criticised the .... violent actions.

believer   A .... faith can be tested when bad things happen.

farmer   Extreme weather can affect a .... livelihood.

Q6   **Without** using an **apostrophe**, write out the **meaning** of the phrases below.

a) the prophet's teachings ⟹ the ...teachings... of the ...prophet...

b) the characters' fears ⟹ the .... of the ....

c) the ministers' decisions ⟹ the .... of the ....

d) the book's themes ⟹ the .... of the ....

e) the glacier's size ⟹ the .... of the ....

f) the city's schools ⟹ the .... of the ....

g) the sources' reliability ⟹ the .... of the ....

h) the play's scenes ⟹ the .... of the ....

i) the soldier's letters ⟹ the .... of the ....

Its and It's

Q1 Write 'it is' or 'it has' in the box to show the meaning of each version of 'it's'.

a) Christmas is a celebration, but some Christians believe **it's** become too commercial.

....

b) The glacier is getting smaller: **it's** been retreating since the 1800s.

....

c) Even though 'Macbeth' was written hundreds of years ago, **it's** still relevant today.

....

d) **It's** been claimed that the government should have acted differently.

....

e) The Sunnah is very important to Muslims; **it's** seen as the model for a correct Muslim life.

....

f) 'Jane Eyre' was a bestseller when it was published, and **it's** still very popular today.

....

Q2 **Circle** the correct option in each of the following sentences.

a) Chamonix is in eastern France; *it's / its* a popular skiing resort.

b) 'Animal Farm' is an allegory: *it's / its* based on real events.

c) During hyperinflation, money lost *it's / its* value very quickly.

d) Alcohol was illegal during prohibition, but many gangs were involved in *it's / its* distribution.

e) Map skills are useful, so *it's / its* worth practising them.

f) The Earth's population is increasing; *it's / its* more than doubled in the last 50 years.

g) Love is a central theme in the play, but *it's / its* other themes include conflict and fate.

h) Polar ice is melting and *it's / its* causing sea levels to rise.

Q3 Read the statements below and write '**true**' or '**false**' on the dotted lines.

a) **It's** is always short for 'it is'. ....

b) **Its** shows that something 'belongs to it'. ....

c) **Its'** shows that something 'belongs to it'. ....

d) **Its** can't be replaced with 'it is' or 'it has'. ....

Apostrophe or not, the presents clearly belonged to the cat.

Its and It's

Q4   Some of these sentences use 'its' and 'it's' incorrectly. **Rewrite** the incorrect sentences so they are correct. If the sentence is already correct, just put a **tick** on the dotted line.

a) Its a good idea to learn the novel's plot well.

....

b) Switzerland gets 60% of its electricity from HEP stations in the Alps.

....

c) Its agreed that the campaign achieved many of its aims.

....

d) Although it's expensive, it's important to have good flood defences.

....

e) The UK is known for it's countryside and it's landmarks.

....

f) Its our responsibility to care for the planet and it's resources.

....

g) Its important to understand poverty and its causes.

....

Q5   Choose between 'it's' and 'its' to complete the following sentences.

a) A synagogue often has symbols on .... outside walls.

b) The text uses images to give .... reader extra information.

c) A ribbon lake is usually long, and .... often very thin.

d) Germany attempted to double the size of .... navy between 1900 and 1914.

e) Robert tells his sister about Victor's experiment and .... a chilling tale.

f) Unilateral disarmament is where just one country gives up .... weapons.

g) If a forest is going to be used in the long term, ... got to be managed in a sustainable way.

h) Agnostics believe .... impossible to know if there's a god or not.

i) The outer layer of the Earth is the crust; .... very thin.

j) Pip goes to Satis House and meets .... inhabitants.

k) A source can be useful, but it will also have .... limitations.

Speech Marks

Q1   Add **speech marks** in the correct places to **complete** these sentences.

a) After the Cold War , the USA was the only superpower , she said .

b) Today we'll be talking about forgiveness , said the priest .

c) She said , The novel has an open ending .

d) There were many factors that led to the Iraq war , said Emily .

e) Many people are concerned about animal rights , he explained .

f) At the end of the show , the crowd cried , Encore !

g) Evil and suffering are sent to test us , said the imam .

h) I asked , What is the US president's name ?

i) Shut up , said Ralph absently .

j) Mary asked , In which continent is Iran ?

k) Read to the end of the chapter , said Miss Phillips .

l) Clive said , Don't believe everything you read !

Q2   Read the statements below and write '**true**' or '**false**' on the dotted lines.

a) Indirect speech doesn't need speech marks.   ....

b) Direct speech always ends with a punctuation mark.   ....

c) A full stop introduces direct speech.   ....

d) Indirect speech records exactly what was said.   ....

e) Direct speech always begins with a capital letter.   ....

Q3   Add **speech marks** and **punctuation** in the correct places to **complete** these sentences.

a) He said The river discharge tells us how much water flows in the river

b) Jane said Zakah is the third Pillar of Islam

c) Comrades shouted the Major

d) Look at me said Miss Havisham

e) When did the Second World War end asked Claire

f) Did they say The ice is melting

g) The Sabbath is a day of rest for animals as well as people I said

h) Has anybody got a copy of the text asked Raj

i) Jo said I'm drawing a timeline of the important events during the war

Speech Marks

Q4   **Tick** the boxes next to the examples where direct speech has been punctuated **correctly**, and **cross** the boxes where it has been punctuated **incorrectly**.

a) "I'm going to get up early tomorrow," Ben said. ☐

b) Ross said, "the hills are covered with snow." ☐

c) Esther asked, "Will you be at the party"? ☐

d) "They've bought a new car," Steve explained. ☐

e) She said "You can take a shortcut to work." ☐

f) "The mouse ate the cheese." I said. ☐

g) "Make sure you do your homework," Dad said. ☐

h) Kieran shouted, "Stop that thief" ☐

Hannah's new friend wasn't very good at finding direct speech.

Now **write out** the incorrect sentences, with the **correct punctuation**.

....

....

....

....

....

Q5   Add **speech marks** and **punctuation** in the correct places to **complete** this dialogue.

Everybody stand up shouted General McGuire as he entered the canteen

Why should we We've only just sat down grumbled Lieutenant Snape

Don't question the General bellowed Colonel Jones

I'll tell you why Someone has taken an extra helping McGuire continued

And we're going to find out who it was exclaimed Jones

Turn out your pockets and hold out your hands said McGuire

My trousers don't have pockets said Snape

Roll up your trouser legs instead replied McGuire

What's that asked Jones as he pointed to Snape's knobbly ankles

Apples stuffed inside his socks shouted McGuire

Speech Marks

Q6 Rewrite the sentences below, adding **speech marks**, **capital letters** and **punctuation** correctly.

a) what are we studying today asked beth

....

b) there is no other option the policeman explained

....

c) poverty leads to great suffering said steve

....

d) this has gone on long enough shouted joanne

....

Q7 **Rewrite** the passage below with the correct punctuation.

I asked Tom if he would listen to my presentation on glacial landforms? He said Okay, but I haven't got long.

When I'd finished, Tom had lots of questions. He asked why do tarns sometimes form in corries.

A corrie is a circular depression in the land, so water collects there to form a tarn I explained.

He also wanted to know some examples of ribbon lakes? I said There are many ribbon lakes, including Windermere in the Lake District.

....

....

....

....

....

....

....

....

....

....

....

Quoting

Q1 **Quote** the underlined sections of the **article** to **complete the essay** below. Make sure you use the correct **punctuation**.

> The people of Bridgeton have a <u>new passion</u>: they are becoming <u>fascinated by bird-watching</u> and identifying birds.
>
> The craze began last summer when local photographer, Rachel Mitchell, attended the annual craft fair. Her <u>beautiful photograph of the common sparrow</u> inspired residents of all ages to take an interest in the town's birds.
>
> Since then, sales of bird feeders have increased as people are trying to attract wrens, chaffinches and blue tits to their gardens.
>
> To make the most of the town's new interest, plans to build a selection of <u>bird boxes and a bird-watching hut</u> in Bridgeton Park are now being discussed.

According to the article, the people of Bridgeton have a ....:

they are becoming ....

The article suggests that the main reason for this was a ....

.... by a local wildlife photographer.

We are also told that this popular hobby has resulted in plans for ....

.... to be built locally.

Q2 **Quote** the underlined sections of the **play** to **complete the essay** below. Make sure you use the correct **punctuation**.

> **Friar Laurence**: How much salt water thrown away in waste,
> To season love, that of it doth not taste!
> The sun not yet thy sighs from heaven clears,
> Thy <u>old groans</u> ring yet in my ancient ears.
> Lo, here <u>upon thy cheek the stain doth sit</u>
> <u>Of an old tear</u> that is not washed off yet.
> If e'er thou wast thyself and these woes thine,
> Thou and these <u>woes</u> were all for Rosaline:
> And art thou changed? Pronounce this sentence then,
> Women may fall, when there's no strength in men.
> ('Romeo and Juliet' by William Shakespeare, Act 2, Scene 3)

"You'll never win this argument, dear — I'm quoting the paper."

Friar Laurence challenges Romeo about how quickly he has moved on from his previous love,

Rosaline. He says that he can still hear Romeo's ...., and suggests that Romeo's

tears for Rosaline are still visible: ....

.... He is trying to remind Romeo of all of his previous ....

Mixed Practice

Q1 **Rewrite** these sentences including **capital letters** and **punctuation** to end the sentence.

a) george orwell wrote 'animal farm'

....

b) the Usa wanted to protect vietnam

....

c) romeo and juliet asked friar laurence for help

....

d) christians believe that god created the world

....

e) what is the purpose of life

....

f) Mount everest is in the himalayas

....

Q2 **Add** a pair of brackets to each of these sentences.

a) Tsunamis large sea waves can be caused by an earthquake or volcanic eruption .

b) Gender roles how men and women should behave are explained in the play .

c) The Weimar Republic was established when Friedrich Ebert came to power 1919 .

d) The nativity story the story of Jesus's birth is told in the Bible .

e) The soil on the island is shallow about 20 cm deep .

f) Make a range of points in your essay one per paragraph .

Barry (left) thought that this grass really needed some ketchup.

Q3 **Add commas** in the correct places in the sentences below.

Tip: some of these sentences need more than one comma.

a) Tourists can bring more traffic to an area which increases pollution.

b) Great Britain France Italy and Spain are all part of Europe.

c) 'Pride and Prejudice' written by Jane Austen was published in 1813.

d) The end of Ramadan the Muslim month of fasting is marked by Eid ul-Fitr.

e) Although it takes time make sure you check your essay for errors.

Mixed Practice

Q4 Add **semicolons** in the correct places in the sentences below.

a) A nuclear family consists of parents and children an extended family includes members of three or more generations.

b) Allah sent many prophets to guide mankind Muhammad was the final prophet.

c) The Munich Agreement was signed in 1938 many British people supported the treaty.

d) Boxer is a principled character he's also the hardest-working animal on the farm.

e) Earthquakes can result in people being trapped in their homes aftershocks can sometimes make rescue attempts difficult.

f) Life in the trenches was very dangerous many soldiers died or were wounded there.

Q5 Some of these sentences use a comma where they should use a **colon**. **Rewrite** them with the **correct punctuation**. If the sentence is correct, just put a **tick** on the dotted line.

a) New jobs were created, the economy was improving.

....

b) The boys can do what they like, there are no adults.

....

c) Muslims try to obey Allah, so they pray five times a day.

....

d) A volcanic eruption can be disastrous, the lava is dangerous.

....

e) The Italians wanted revenge on Abyssinia, so Mussolini invaded the country.

....

f) People were not treated equally, prejudice was widespread.

....

Q6 **Complete** the sentences by adding **apostrophes** where necessary.

Tip: some sentences need more than one apostrophe.

a) Sheila feels that she should find out whos responsible for the womans death.

b) Lenins strong leadership was one reason for his partys success.

c) Youll find that a rivers cross profile varies over its course.

d) Paranormal events are things that science cant explain, such as ghosts.

e) Ive never seen 'Macbeth' on stage, but Id love to see it.

Mixed Practice

Q7 **Rewrite** these sentences, adding **hyphens** in the correct places.

a) I found the saucepan lid and recovered the food.

....

b) The prodemocracy movement was unsuccessful.

....

c) The pre1941 agreement was broken.

....

d) I had to deice the car windscreen before I left work.

....

e) The troops reentered the city at night.

....

Q8 Add **speech marks** and other **punctuation** in the correct places to **complete** these sentences.

a) Good   morning,   sir   called   the   greengrocer   .

b) The   King   said   You   have   my   word   .

c) Can   I   see   some   evidence   he   asked   .

d) She   said   The   Earth   spins   on   an   axis   .

e) Luke   said   I   liked   the   main   character   .

f) Joseph   whispered   It's   time   to   go   .

g) Where   shall   we   go   for   lunch   she   asked   .

h) Everyone   shouted   Hooray   !

Harry and Jake couldn't work out where
to put the speech marks.

Q9 **Circle** the correct option in each of the following sentences.

a) The *Earths / Earth's* population is increasing and *we're / were* running out of many resources.

b) Jesus fed 5 000 people using a young *boys / boy's* five *loaves / loave's* and two fish.

c) Martin Luther King campaigned for African *Americans' / American's* civil *right's / rights*.

d) Juliet is a young girl *whose / who's* family is the enemy of *Romeo's / Romeos'* family.

e) The Inspector *lets / let's* the *Birlings / Birlings'* grow suspicious of each other.

f) *Nobodys / Nobody's* going to remember, so we'll have to do it ourselves.

Mixed Practice

Q10 Choose between 'it's' and 'its' to **complete** the following sentences.

    a) Some people argue that being a good person has .... own rewards.

    b) At the end of the play, ... not clear who the Inspector was.

    c) There are ways to reduce traffic and .... impacts.

    d) When people move to a country, ... called immigration.

    e) The Nazi party set up .... own armed group called the SA.

    f) Muslims won't eat chicken unless .... been butchered in a special way.

    g) Each river in a drainage basin has .... own valley.

    h) Watching film adaptations of books is useful, but .... dangerous to rely on them too much.

Q11 These sentences contain some comma mistakes. **Circle** the incorrect commas, and **add** in the missing ones.

    a) Estella, Miss Havisham's adopted daughter makes Pip, feel common.

    b) By the end of 1914 there were trenches, between Belgium's coast and Switzerland.

    c) Flood engineering strategies such as flood warnings can reduce the effects, of flooding.

    d) Christianity Judaism, and Islam, all teach that a love of wealth is bad.

    e) If you use a wide, range of vocabulary you'll impress the examiner.

    f) Macbeth is responsible, for the deaths of Banquo Lady Macduff and King Duncan.

Q12 **Rewrite** these sentences adding **capital letters** and the correct **punctuation**.

    a) when you read a novel think about its setting

    ....

    b) during the 1960s anti war conventions were held in the USA

    ....

    c) nigeria and cameroon are african countries

    ....

    d) wait for the others said Marcus

    ....

    e) world War Two 1939-1945 involved many countries.

    ....

Section Three — Grammar

Pronouns

Q1 Underline all the **pronouns** in the sentences below, and then write the pronouns that show **possession** in the box.

a) There have been major changes in the way we shop in the UK in the last 100 years.

b) Television affects concentration — yours included — so switch it off when revising.

c) Break the information down into smaller pieces, learning them one at a time.

d) The Qur'an states Allah's mercy means he will help us with any problems.

e) Julie gave me the phone number, and I let her have mine.

f) There was no label on the cake, so they didn't know if it was his or hers.

g) The scriptures were written against a different cultural background from ours.

Pronouns that show possession

Q2 Complete the sentences below by adding **pronouns** correctly:

a) The homework is mine — it belongs to ....

b) The shoes are .... — they belong to them.

c) The car is yours — it belongs to ....

d) The book is .... — it belongs to her.

e) The dog is ours — it belongs to ....

f) The laptop is .... — it belongs to him.

Ben and the lads went looking
for possessive pronouns.
They found a mine.

Q3 **Rewrite** the sentences by replacing the underlined words with the correct **pronoun** in brackets.

a) <u>Stalin</u> *(He/Him/His)* instructed <u>his scientists</u> *(their/they/them)* to begin work on an A-bomb.

....

b) <u>The Enabling Act</u> *(He/Its/It)* gave <u>Hitler</u> *(he/him/his)* the powers of a dictator.

....

c) <u>Catholics</u> *(Their/They/Them)* pray to <u>Mary</u> *(she/her/hers)* and ask <u>Mary</u> *(she/her/hers)* for help.

....

d) <u>Paula and I</u> *(Us/We/Our)* ran to <u>Viv's house</u> *(she/her/hers)* on Monday evening.

....

Pronouns

Q4 **Complete** the sentences below using a suitable **pronoun** to replace the person or thing in **italics**:

a) *Mary* is very important to Christians because .... gave birth to Jesus.

b) You need to know your *facts* and you've got to be able to explain .... clearly.

c) *Earthquakes* might seem exciting, but .... can be life-threatening.

d) When you read *a poem*, think about why the poet wrote ....

Q5 **Complete** the sentences below using a **possessive pronoun** to replace the words in brackets.

a) I respect your beliefs, so you should respect .... *(my beliefs)*

b) We ate at my house yesterday — let's eat at .... *(your house)* tonight.

c) That's not our report; it's .... *(their report)*

d) They gave a very good presentation, but .... *(our presentation)* was better.

Q6 **Rewrite** the sentences in italics by replacing the underlined nouns with a suitable **pronoun**.

a) God made a promise to the people. *<u>God</u> said that <u>the people</u> would find salvation if <u>the people</u> followed <u>God's</u> teaching.*

....

....

b) Martin Luther King used peaceful protests. *<u>Peaceful protests</u> enabled <u>Martin Luther King</u> to gain publicity for <u>Martin Luther King's</u> cause.*

....

....

Q7 Tick the sentences below which use '**I**' and '**me**' **correctly**.

a) The team and I are travelling to Scotland for our next away game. ☐

b) Between you and I, I don't think the company's new approach is working. ☐

c) Ahmed travelled to work with Elizabeth and I. ☐

d) Me and the dogs got lost on a walk across the Yorkshire Dales. ☐

e) Rasheed and I are planning to expand our business next year. ☐

f) Me and Lisa are going on holiday to America. ☐

Who, Which and That

Q1 Underline the words in italics that complete the sentences **correctly**:

a) The Earth's surface is made of huge floating plates *that / who* are constantly moving.

b) Some people claim Lenin was a quick-thinking leader *which / who* inspired his party.

c) A democratic process is any way in *which / that* citizens can help to run a country.

d) Around the Earth's core is the mantle, *who / which* is semi-molten rock that moves very slowly.

e) Some workers quit, and those *which / that* remained were forced to accept a pay cut.

f) Some people were given the job of scaring the pigeons *which / who* were causing a nuisance.

g) Through rehabilitation, an offender can learn a trade, *who / which* helps their self-esteem.

Q2 Add '**who**' or '**which**' **correctly** to the questions below:

a) .... became president in 1921?

b) .... Christian denomination believes in Purgatory?

c) .... was Nelson Mandela?

d) .... American president came up with the Fourteen Points?

Which witch is this?

Q3 Use your **answers** to questions **1** and **2** to complete the **rules** below with a word from the **box**:

a) Use .... when you are talking about people.

b) Use .... when you are talking about animals or things.

c) You can use .... to refer to things or people.

d) You can use .... and .... when you ask a question.

which
that
who

Q4 Add '**who**', '**which**' or '**that**' **correctly** to the sentences below.
There may be **more than one** correct answer for some sentences.

a) Access routes improve communications for people .... live in that area.

b) Check with your teacher .... topics you should revise for your exams.

c) Governments can limit the number of people .... are allowed to immigrate.

d) Tax credits support parents .... go back to work after their children are born.

e) Make sure you read and understand the comments .... are written in red.

f) Christians believe that it was Jesus's death on the cross .... won the battle against sin.

g) An agnostic is someone .... believes it's impossible to know whether there's a god.

h) Some believe it was the one-child policy .... slowed population growth in China.

Who or Whom, Who's or Whose

Q1   Underline the words in italics that complete the sentences **correctly**:

a) During the war, Germany's enemy was Britain, *whose / who's* empire and navy it envied.

b) Austria-Hungary was made up of 10 nationalities, many of *who / whom* wanted independence.

c) The chief priests and elders asked Jesus on *whose / who's* authority he was acting.

d) The person in *who / whom* I confided was a close friend of mine.

e) Catholics often pray to a saint on behalf of someone *whose / who's* suffering.

f) Loans were provided for people *who's / whose* homes were in danger of being repossessed.

g) Helping those *who / whom* are in need is seen as a key part of various faiths.

Q2   Circle the **mistakes** in the sentences below.
Then write out each sentence **correctly** on the dotted lines.

a) Countries who's industries were weak bought American goods.

....

b) The sources disagree about whom started the fire.

....

c) The photo shows two men, both of who were politicians.

....

d) The clergy consists of anyone whose been ordained.

....

Q3   Add a word from the box **correctly** to the sentences below.

who	whom	who's	whose

a) Governments make alliances with foreign leaders .... share their ideas.

b) A hypocrite is a person .... actions don't match what they say.

c) During a flood, rescue boats are usually sent to help people .... are stranded.

d) The campsite was so dark, I couldn't tell which tent belonged to ....

e) The Bible states divorce is only permitted to someone .... partner has been unfaithful.

f) Critics say it is hard to guess .... going to win the film award.

g) At funerals, the life of the person .... died is usually celebrated.

h) The police want to find the witness .... wanted in connection with the crime.

i) After the argument, no one could remember who said what to ....

Verbs

Q1 Underline the **verbs** in the **simple present tense** and circle the **subjects** in the sentences below.
Hint: the **subject** is the person or thing doing the action. It might be more than one word long.

The simple present tense is the basic form of a verb, e.g. I walk, he runs, they are.

a) Priests are in charge of Catholic worship and education in their parish.

b) Visitors damage forests by causing erosion and disturbing wildlife.

c) Scientists usually publish their findings in scientific journals.

d) Warm, moist air from the tropics meets cold, dry air from the poles.

e) Many people in poor countries depend on farming.

f) In most Muslim communities, parents search for suitable partners for their children.

g) The Qur'an describes Jahannam as a place of scorching fire, hot winds and black smoke.

h) Military forces need the best available equipment for their troops.

Q2 Circle the words in **italics** that complete the sentences so that the **verb** and **subject** agree:

a) During droughts, soil, which is sometimes made up of clay and rock particles, *dry / dries* out.

b) An electrical phenomenon, such as static electricity or lightning, *are / is* fairly commonplace.

c) First aid training, designed to teach life-saving skills, *focus / focuses* on a variety of things.

d) A layer of undergrowth, including brambles and mosses, *cover / covers* the entire area.

e) The community of several thousand people *reject / rejects* the proposal.

f) Many scientists, such as Stephen Hawking, *believe / believes* science governs the universe.

g) Discriminatory behaviour, including racism and ageism, *contradicts / contradict* our ethics.

h) The recruitment process, contrary to recent criticisms, *play / plays* an important role.

Q3 **Change** the **underlined singular** nouns into **plural** nouns and rewrite the sentences.

Make sure the verb agrees with the subject.

a) A banana contains roughly fourteen grams of sugar.

....

b) A religious person usually goes to church regularly.

....

c) A cyclist rides along the road or the cycle path.

....

d) The current is faster on the outside of the bend.

....

e) The politician has many supporters.

....

Forming the Present Tense

Q1 Write out the **third person simple present tense** form of the verbs in **brackets**:

a) he .... *(fly)*

b) she .... *(confess)*

c) Mike .... *(argue)*

d) it .... *(cry)*

e) Julie .... *(travel)*

f) it .... *(rely)*

g) she .... *(address)*

h) he .... *(reply)*

Q2 Add the **simple present tense** form of the **verb** in brackets correctly to the sentences below:

a) Some of the players .... taking penalties. *(to enjoy)*

b) The government .... many civil servants. *(to employ)*

c) Jesus .... up with his disciples' boat by walking across the water. *(to catch)*

d) The roots of a desert plant usually .... deep underground to find water. *(to reach)*

e) Our family .... to have great holidays on a budget. *(to try)*

f) The Nile .... north from East Africa to the Mediterranean. *(to stretch)*

g) David .... the constellations in the sky. *(to study)*

h) The jury .... the accused is innocent. *(to believe)*

i) Romeo .... back to Verona when he thinks Juliet is dead. *(to hurry)*

j) The rising sea level .... coastal habitats. *(to destroy)*

Q3 Complete the **table** below with the correct **simple present tense** forms of the **verbs**:

Verb	I	You (singular)	He/She/It	We	You (plural)	They
to be						
to have						

Q4 Add the correct **simple present tense** form of the verb '**to be**' to the sentences below:

a) The Earth's surface .... separated into tectonic plates.

b) In an Orthodox wedding, crowns .... placed on the heads of the bride and groom.

c) A worker on strike told the interviewer, "I .... unhappy with the working conditions."

d) Macbeth and Banquo .... soldiers in the Scottish army.

e) Christians believe that we .... all responsible for caring for the planet.

f) The Friar .... persuaded to help Romeo and Juliet.

Forming -ing Verbs

Q1 Form the **present tense** with '**-ing**' for the verb '**to write**'.

a) I ....

b) You ....

c) He ....

d) We ....

e) You ....

f) They ....

Q2 Form the **past tense** with '**ing**' for the verb '**to lie**'.

a) I ....

b) You ....

c) She ....

d) We ....

e) You ....

f) They ....

Q3 Fill in the **gaps** with the **past tense** of '**to be**' and underline the correct spelling of the words in **italics**.

a) The poster shows that the soldiers .... *driving / driveing* the enemy away.

b) Increased traffic meant the narrow roads .... *developping / developing* potholes.

c) During hyperinflation, people .... *buiing / buying* items with bags full of money.

d) One witness said the ground .... *shaking / shakeing* violently during the earthquake.

e) The fans .... *applauding / applaudding* enthusiastically, so the band played more songs.

f) In the 1930s, women .... *embracing / embraceing* roles traditionally fulfilled by men.

g) I .... *debateing / debating* whether or not to apply for the job vacancy.

h) The Labour MP .... *appealing / appealling* to the Conservative MP for a straight answer.

i) Protesters .... *targetting / targeting* the main government buildings.

Q4 Rewrite the sentences below in the **present tense** with '**-ing**'.

a) He addresses the congregation. ....

b) Aid workers travel to Africa. ....

c) The Earth's plates move. ....

d) I help those in need. ....

e) The event promotes justice. ....

f) You complicate matters. ....

g) Builders level the road. ....

h) They consider the outcome. ....

Forming -ing Verbs

Q5 **Complete** each sentence below using the **present tense** with 'ing' form of the verb in brackets:

a) People .... to recycle more of their rubbish. *(to begin)*

b) I .... the site of a World War One battlefield. *(to visit)*

c) Melika .... her piggy bank to find another coin. *(to shake)*

d) The cheeky children .... the teacher. *(to annoy)*

e) The men and women .... separately. *(to dance)*

f) Army leaders do not believe their troops .... the war. *(to win)*

g) The risk of coastal flooding .... greater. *(to become)*

h) The airline .... the number of flights to Poland. *(to double)*

Q6 **Rewrite** the passage below with the correct **past tense** with '-ing' form of the verb in brackets:

In the boardroom, the managers *(to discuss)* whether to alter the menu in the canteen, but not everyone *(to pay)* attention. Mr May *(to tap)* away on his phone, whilst Miss Cross *(to stare)* out of the window. The two new accountants *(to chat)* and Mrs Gray *(to tidy)* her handbag.

....

....

....

....

....

....

Q7 **Complete** each sentence below using the **'-ing' tense** and the **verb** shown in brackets:

a) The refugees of war .... from the threat of violence. *(past + to flee)*

b) Don't forget to say which religion you .... to. *(present + to refer)*

c) Air-raid sirens warned citizens that an attack .... *(past + to come)*

d) A group of scientists .... the Big Bang theory. *(present + to challenge)*

e) The climber .... knots in the rope. *(present + to tie)*

f) The driver .... the speed limit. *(past + to break)*

g) Emergency aid helps those who .... from starvation. *(present + to die)*

h) Victory banners and flags .... on the rooftops. *(past + to flap)*

The Simple Past

Q1   Write the **simple past tense** forms of the verbs below.

a) become   ....   **i)** hurt   ....

b) know   ....   **j)** sleep   ....

c) celebrate   ....   **k)** demand   ....

d) honour   ....   **l)** study   ....

e) wear   ....   **m)** meet   ....

f) behave   ....   **n)** travel   ....

g) drop   ....   **o)** find   ....

h) hope   ....   **p)** die   ....

Q2   Circle the verbs below that are **irregular** in the **simple past tense**.
Then write the **simple past tense** forms of these verbs in the box below.

Tommy took 'I spy'
very seriously.

eat	steal	tempt	practise	see
publish	have	take	repair	attend
make	oppose	plant	give	drink

Q3   Circle the words in italics that complete the sentences **correctly**:

a) Most urbanisation in rich countries *occurred* / *occured* during the Industrial Revolution.

b) The doctor *admitted* / *admited* to giving the patient a higher dosage of medication.

c) Farmers *worryed* / *worried* that their crops would fail due to the flood.

d) The former employee was *imprisoned* / *imprisonned* for lying in court.

e) The researchers *identified* / *identifyed* several problems with the data.

f) Indochina was a French colony that *covered* / *coverred* a large area of South-East Asia.

g) Droughts are often *accompanied* / *accompanyed* by high temperatures.

The Simple Past

Q4   Add the **simple past tense** form of the verbs in **brackets** to complete the sentences below:

a) Parliament .... the law and the courts enforced it. *(to make)*

b) During the Depression, some people .... hard to keep their pride. *(to fight)*

c) The Antarctic Treaty is an agreement that .... into force in 1961. *(to come)*

d) Mother Teresa .... an Albanian Roman Catholic nun. *(to be)*

e) Quaternary industry is sometimes .... of as a part of tertiary industry. *(to think)*

f) All women over 21 .... the vote in 1928. *(to get)*

g) Hurricane Mitch .... Nicaragua in 1998. *(to hit)*

h) The Depression almost certainly .... Hoover the 1932 election. *(to cost)*

i) Anne Frank's diary describes how her family .... from the Nazis. *(to hide)*

j) The Reformation .... when Martin Luther challenged the Pope's authority. *(to begin)*

k) After the storm, exports of rice .... down as crops were damaged. *(to go)*

Q5   Rewrite the sentences below so that they are in the **simple past tense**:

a) The company withholds some information.

   ....

b) We do our best at the Summer Championships.

   ....

c) They transfer money between accounts.

   ....

d) Fairtrade schemes pay farmers a fair price.

   ....

Q6   Circle the **mistakes** in the passage below and write the **corrections** in the box.

A theatre group putted on a production of 'My Fair Lady' last night. The cast sold every single ticket before the show, which beated all expectations. The local press reviewwed the performance. One critic writed, "It's not surprising the play bringed in a large crowd — the actors sanged beautifully and catched the audience's full attention."

The Past Tense with 'Have'

Q1   Form the **past tense** with '**have**' of the verbs in **brackets** to complete the sentences below:

   a) They .... an explosion. *(to hear)*

   b) You .... a caravan. *(to rent)*

   c) He .... it. *(to explain)*

   d) I .... the meeting early. *(to leave)*

   e) We .... to go. *(to decide)*

   f) She .... to do her best. *(to promise)*

   g) It .... apparent that we're losing. *(to become)*

   h) We .... the books back to the library. *(to take)*

Q2   Write down the verbs below in their **past tense** with '**have**' forms.

a) I went	....	**k)** it left	....
b) you told	....	**l)** it fell	....
c) he bit	....	**m)** you gave	....
d) they won	....	**n)** he forgot	....
e) we blew	....	**o)** they drank	....
f) she built	....	**p)** she heard	....
g) I chose	....	**q)** I fled	....
h) we came	....	**r)** we froze	....
i) it cost	....	**s)** I grew	....
j) you drew	....	**t)** they knew	....

Q3   The sentences below are **incorrect**. Rewrite them using the **past tense** with '**have**' **correctly**.

   a) They been fighting a lot.   ....

   b) You gone the wrong way.   ....

   c) I done the washing-up.   ....

   d) We seen the film.   ....

   e) She have taken the car.   ....

   f) Jane been to France.   ....

   g) He done his homework.   ....

   h) I has made a mistake.   ....

The Past Tense with 'Have'

Q4   Rewrite the sentences below so they are in the **past tense** with **'have'**.

a) His friends forgave him for his mistake.

....

b) The rain fell over the hills.

....

c) The factory workers did lots of overtime.

....

d) The choir sang the hymns.

....

e) The urban population grew quickly.

....

Q5   Circle the correct word in **italics** in each of these sentences so that they make sense:

a) In times *of / have* recession, people tend to cut back on luxuries.

b) No organisation could *of / have* stopped leaders like Mussolini or Hitler peacefully.

c) It would *of / have* taken years for the country to pay off its debt.

d) Prayer can be thought *of / have* as a conversation with God.

e) There are many reasons why businesses might *of / have* rejected the deal.

f) Wedding guests are asked if they know *of / have* any reason why the couple should not marry.

Q6   Form the **past tense** with **'have'** of the verbs in **brackets** to complete the sentences below:

a) The birds .... the seeds planted by the farmer. *(to eat)*

b) The players .... the game and are returning home. *(to lose)*

c) If the criminal .... the law, the punishment will be severe. *(to break)*

d) Roger .... the eggs and is now sifting the flour. *(to beat)*

e) The aid workers .... 2 000 miles to reach Syria. *(to drive)*

f) Some prisoners .... what it's like to be free citizens. *(to forget)*

g) Your opinion may be affected by what you .... *(to read)*

h) The Prime Minister .... to the German Chancellor. *(to speak)*

i) The First and Second World Wars .... us many lessons. *(to teach)*

j) Limiting visitor access .... the impact of tourism low. *(to keep)*

Negatives

Q1 Underline the **negative words** in these sentences.
Cross the ones which have a **double negative** and **tick** the ones that are **correct**.

a) There doesn't seem to be no reason for the conflict. ☐

b) Nothing could prepare them for what happened. ☐

c) We don't know none of the people over there. ☐

d) There's nowhere quite like the Shetland Islands. ☐

e) I am not telling nobody about my new hobby. ☐

f) The American people never accepted the Treaty of Versailles. ☐

*Phil the photographer had a
negative outlook on life...*

Rewrite the sentences you **crossed** so that they are **correct**.

....

....

....

Q2 Circle the **most appropriate** word in italics to complete the sentences below correctly:

a) The government didn't accept *no / any* foreign aid.

b) It was called the Cold War because there wasn't *any / no* direct fighting.

c) The governor *never / didn't* discuss the matter with *anybody / nobody*.

d) They decided not to share *no / any* information with *no one / anyone*.

e) We want to donate some old clothes, but we don't have *any / none*.

f) Wild kangaroos can't be found *nowhere / anywhere* in the UK.

g) There isn't *anything / nothing* we can do to turn back time.

h) There's no chance of finding *anything / nothing* useful in a blank book.

Q3 The sentences below are **incorrect**. Rewrite them using **negatives** correctly.

a) There ain't no sharks in the lake. ....

b) I ain't got no problem with that. ....

c) He ain't the boss — I am. ....

d) Kim ain't seen the new play. ....

e) We ain't got time to go there. ....

f) Tim ain't never going to change. ....

g) You ain't met nobody like Olga. ....

Negatives

Q4 Complete the **table** below with either '**doesn't**' or '**don't**'.

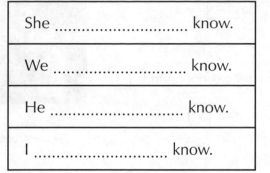

She .... know.	They .... know.
We .... know.	You .... know.
He .... know.	It .... know.
I .... know.	

Q5 Add either '**doesn't**' or '**don't**' to complete the sentences below:

a) Predicting a volcanic eruption .... stop buildings being destroyed.

b) Many hospitals in poorer countries .... have enough supplies.

c) .... take sources at face value — look at what a source really means.

d) I .... judge people by how they look, but by how they behave.

e) Preparation .... guarantee safety from a flood.

f) Atheists .... believe in a god.

g) We .... usually rely on others for help.

h) In the Bible, Jesus .... just talk about forgiveness.

Q6 Rewrite the sentences below using '**don't**' or '**doesn't**' to make them negative.

a) The UK has a rainforest. ....

b) Unemployed people work. ....

c) We complain about the noise. ....

d) I feel very well. ....

e) Malcolm attends Mass. ....

f) Our horse likes carrots. ....

g) The manager agrees with us. ....

h) Money grows on trees. ....

i) Vegetarians eat meat. ....

j) Tim and Tina have a pet. ....

Staying in the Right Tense

Q1 **Tick** the sentences below that use **tenses** correctly and **cross** those that don't.

a) The teachers will go on strike in two day's time. ☐

b) Advent begins two weeks ago. ☐

c) The festival has been cancelled and we have received a refund. ☐

d) I am reading a book whilst Liam listened to music. ☐

Remember — stay in the right tent, not the left one.

Q2 Draw a clear **line** through the **verbs** that are in the **wrong tense** and write the correct version above.

a) Last Saturday, there was a torrential downpour and many towns flood.

b) In today's world, many people live and worked in terrible conditions.

c) When the boats landed yesterday, the troops swim ashore.

d) By this time tomorrow, the two leaders have met to discuss the crisis and will have resolved it.

e) Last month, the town hall clock broke, so the mayor fixes it and reset the time.

f) Environmentalists will sign a petition next week and they have posted it to their MP.

g) I followed the plan in my last exam, and I leave time to check my work.

The verb might be made up of more than one word.

Q3 Underline the words in *italics* that complete the passage below correctly.

The Model T was a motorcar that was first produced in 1908. It *becomes / became* the first affordable motorcar that *made / is making* it possible for middle-class American families to travel freely. Henry Ford *produced / is producing* this vehicle using assembly line production, and by 1927 he *sees / saw* the fifteen millionth Model T roll off his assembly line. In 1914, Ford *will decide / decided* to only make this model available in black, which perhaps *helped / had helped* to keep production costs down.

Q4 Draw lines to **correctly** match the **first** parts of the sentences below to the **second** parts.

a) They will go to the theatre   i) and we are walking there now.

b) I went to the theatre   ii) she always watches the same play.

c) We are going to the theatre   iii) and he was planning to watch the play.

d) He was going to the theatre   iv) although I had already seen the play.

e) Whenever she goes to the theatre,   v) and you have watched the play.

f) You have been to the theatre   vi) and they will watch the play.

Staying in the Right Tense

Q5   Add the **verbs** in brackets to the sentences below by putting them into the **correct tense**.

    a) Some people live in villages and .... to work in urban areas. *(to commute)*

    b) German forces had orders to pull out if the French army .... in. *(to move)*

    c) In 2006, Zambia .... enough money to offer free health care. *(to have)*

    d) The rabbi will read from the Torah and he .... a sermon. *(to give)*

    e) We will clear out your room and Dad .... your things to the tip. *(to take)*

    f) The cross is a Christian symbol which .... Jesus's crucifixion. *(to represent)*

    g) The world's population is increasing — it .... rapidly. *(to grow)*

    h) In 2004, ten eastern European countries .... the EU. *(to join)*

    i) The nature reserve .... thousands of visitors in 2011. *(to attract)*

    j) Within days, lots of money had been pledged and work .... *(to begin)*

    k) My workload is shrinking — the pile on my desk .... smaller. *(to get)*

    l) Cody .... Brad's car keys and didn't tell him. *(to hide)*

    m) A conundrum .... a confusing or difficult problem. *(to be)*

Q6   Write out these sentences, **making changes** to the **tense** of the **verbs** where necessary:

    a) The tsunami destroyed towns and 1.7 million people were losing their homes.

    ....

    ....

    b) Currently, we are raising money and we encouraged people to buy Fairtrade products.

    ....

    ....

    c) By the end of May, the army had interrogated 100 soldiers and it has imprisoned 142 others.

    ....

    ....

    d) The Last Post ceremony takes place every day at 8 pm in Ypres and attracted lots of visitors.

    ....

    ....

    e) We will announce the reforms tomorrow, but it is expected that the workers rejected them.

    ....

    ....

Paragraphs

Q1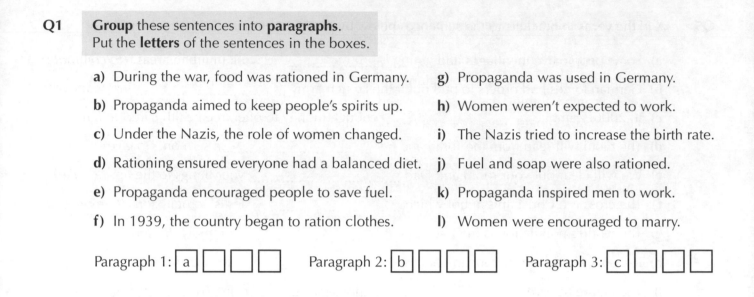

Group these sentences into **paragraphs**.
Put the **letters** of the sentences in the boxes.

a) During the war, food was rationed in Germany.

b) Propaganda aimed to keep people's spirits up.

c) Under the Nazis, the role of women changed.

d) Rationing ensured everyone had a balanced diet.

e) Propaganda encouraged people to save fuel.

f) In 1939, the country began to ration clothes.

g) Propaganda was used in Germany.

h) Women weren't expected to work.

i) The Nazis tried to increase the birth rate.

j) Fuel and soap were also rationed.

k) Propaganda inspired men to work.

l) Women were encouraged to marry.

Paragraph 1: a ☐ ☐ ☐   Paragraph 2: b ☐ ☐ ☐   Paragraph 3: c ☐ ☐ ☐

Q2 Read the passage below, then make things **clearer** by putting in some helpful **paragraph markers** (//):

The first tennis championships at Wimbledon took place in 1877, when twenty-two men paid one pound and one shilling to take part.   These participants were told to bring their own rackets and to wear shoes without heels.   Balls, however, were provided.   In 1884, women were permitted to play in their own championships.   However, play could only begin once the men's singles had been completed.   A female player from the United States called May Sutton became the first overseas entrant to be crowned champion.   She won the tournament in 1905 and went on to win it again in 1907.   May's entry showed that international players were willing to travel to London to take part in the championships.   The popularity of tennis tournaments spread far and wide, and today tournaments take place across the globe.   This means professional players must be willing to travel long distances and thereby dedicate their lives to the game. As one famous player states, "For me, playing tennis is not just a career; it is a way of life."

Q3 Read the passage below, then make things **clearer** by putting in some helpful **paragraph markers** (//):

At the end of the Second World War, Germany and Berlin were divided into zones shared between the Allies.   Russia controlled East Germany and East Berlin, whilst America, France and Britain controlled West Germany and West Berlin.   As time went by, relations between Russia and America deteriorated, and the Cold War began.   The term 'Cold War' came about because there wasn't any direct fighting between these two powers.   Russia and America were, however, making plans and alliances that the other disagreed with.   Over in East Germany and East Berlin, communism firmly gripped the nation, whilst capitalism was the ruling ideology in western parts. A communist lifestyle did not appeal to most citizens, and many decided to flee to the West through Berlin.   In 1961, the Berlin Wall was put up to prevent East Germans from escaping to the West.   This consisted of a concrete barrier with barbed wire and machine gun watchtowers.

Paragraphs

Q4 Rewrite the passage below adding **paragraphs** correctly.

Volcanic lightning is when lightning is produced in a volcanic plume. It's a rare weather phenomenon where two forces of nature, a volcanic eruption and lightning, can be seen at once. Volcanic lightning has been witnessed at almost 200 eruptions over the past 200 years. Dr Higman, a geologist, has photographed dramatic images of volcanic lightning. His photos depict an eruption at Mount Redoubt in Alaska. On 17th April 2010, volcanic lightning occurred at Eyjafjallajökull, Iceland. This particular volcanic eruption began on 14th April and became famous for causing major disruption to air travel across Europe.

....
....
....
....
....
....
....
....
....
....
....
....
....
....
....
....
....

Q5 Circle the correct **option** in italics to explain **why** you started each new paragraph in **Q4**.

a) I started the second paragraph because the text mentions a new *time / place / person*.

b) I started the third paragraph because the text mentions a new *time / place / person*.

Mixed Practice

Q1 Write the verb in brackets in the **same** tense as the **underlined** verb in each sentence.

a) A donor country <u>is</u> a country that .... aid to another country. *(to give)*

b) During the tournament, one team <u>won</u> and seven teams .... *(to lose)*

c) We <u>carried</u> out some research and .... all the evidence. *(to compile)*

d) The population <u>is shrinking</u> because people .... fewer children. *(to have)*

e) He <u>had told</u> him that he .... his driving test. *(to pass)*

f) They <u>approved</u> the plans and the building work .... *(to start)*

g) I <u>tolerate</u> animal experimentation, but only if it .... mankind. *(to benefit)*

h) The forest <u>has gone</u> and the number of endangered species .... *(to rise)*

i) We <u>were listening</u> whilst the mayor .... *(to speak)*

j) The sun <u>is shining</u>, the birds are singing and people .... *(to sunbathe)*

Q2 Complete the **table** below:

simple past tense	past tense with '**have**'
You rode your horse.	I .... my horse.
He .... 10 miles.	We have run 10 miles.
Her foot	My foot has swollen.
The dog woke up.	The cat .... up.
We .... the lawn.	They have mown the lawn.

Sue's been practising medicine for 10 years. One day she hopes to get it right...

Q3 Rewrite the sentences below using '**don't**' and '**doesn't**' to make them **negative**.

a) She has a car. ....

b) We work during the day. ....

c) I play the tuba. ....

d) He believes in fairies. ....

e) They work together. ....

f) Sam goes to the gym. ....

Mixed Practice

Q4 Add a word from the **box** to complete the sentences below **correctly**.
There may be **more than one** correct answer for some sentences.

Only use each word once.

| who | which | that | whom | who's | whose |

a) The party had many supporters, many of .... pledged generous donations.

b) Fold mountain areas have lots of high mountains, ... are very rocky with steep slopes.

c) Hitler was a German leader .... hatred of the Jews had catastrophic consequences.

d) Most people have their own opinion about .... been the best president to date.

e) Upland areas in the Alps are used to farm goats .... provide milk, cheese and meat.

f) It's difficult to say .... was responsible for the Reichstag Fire.

Q5 Put a **tick** on the line for the sentences that are **correct** and **rewrite** those that are **incorrect**.

a) The ship has sunk. ....

b) I spoken to him already. ....

c) He has stole a pencil. ....

d) Karl has been to university. ....

e) We have wrote a letter. ....

f) They have thrown a party. ....

g) It could of gone wrong. ....

h) The dough has rose. ....

i) I have made a mistake. ....

j) She has forget her money. ....

Q6 Circle the **correct word** in italics to complete the sentences below:

a) By the end of Act Three, Scene One, Romeo has *been / being* banished from Verona.

b) In some religions, suffering is *seen / seeing* as a test of faith.

c) Some developing countries are *seen / seeing* massive industrial growth.

d) Mussolini had *been / being* made Prime Minister in 1922 after threatening to march on Rome.

e) A lot of Spain's energy is *been / being* produced using wind turbines.

f) After the Russian Revolution, communism was *seen / seeing* as a serious threat.

g) Some ecosystems are *been / being* threatened by poorly-managed tourism.

Section Three — Grammar

Mixed Practice

Q7 Complete the table below with the **present** and **past tense** with '**ing**' forms of the verbs:

verb	present tense with 'ing'	past tense with 'ing'
to stop	you	they ....
to panic	I	he ....
to create	we	I ....
to party	she	you ....
to progress	they	it ....

Q8 The tenses in the passage below **aren't consistent**. Rewrite it with the **correct tenses**:

Advent marks the start of the Christian year, and began four Sundays before Christmas. It had been a period of preparation for Christmas. People light Advent candles in homes and churches, and children may used Advent calendars to count off the days until Christmas. Christians celebrate Christmas on December 25th, but December 26th was also a bank holiday in England.

....

....

....

....

....

....

....

Q9 **Complete** the sentences below using a suitable **pronoun** that refers back to the word in **italics**:

a) Most people believe *a woman* should be able to choose whom .... marries.

b) *Charles Dickens* was 58 years old when .... died in 1870.

c) *I've* applied for the job and .... am waiting to hear that they've received my CV.

d) When *the troops* retreated, ... didn't have time to get back into their trenches.

e) *I* don't really mind whether we take your car or .... to the horse show.

f) In *your* revision of this topic, make sure .... learn all of the key facts.

g) Free will allows *us* to choose whether .... do good or evil with our lives.

Mixed Practice

Q10 The sentences below are **incorrect**. Rewrite them using **negatives correctly**.

a) There's never been no trouble in this area.

....

b) There don't seem to be any reason to go to war.

....

c) We ain't discussed a solution to the problem yet.

....

d) The weapons weren't nowhere to be seen.

....

e) I doesn't intend to join in the protest.

....

f) They don't know nothing about the benefits system.

....

Q11 Add the correct **simple present tense** form of the **verb** in brackets to the sentences below:

a) In parts of Australia, armed robbery .... a maximum sentence of 25 years. *(to carry)*

b) Judaism .... that we have free will and are able to choose what we do. *(to teach)*

c) 'Bulldozing' is when the ice of a glacier .... loose material in front of it. *(to push)*

d) The interviewer .... celebrities about their professional and private lives. *(to quiz)*

e) When a chef .... an egg, the proteins in the egg white move vigorously. *(to fry)*

f) Condensation .... as warm air rises, causing rain clouds to develop. *(to occur)*

g) In rainforests, the soil isn't very fertile as heavy rain .... nutrients away. *(to wash)*

h) The Jewish faith .... the idea that good can come out of terrible suffering. *(to stress)*

i) A sensible pupil .... exam-style questions during their revision. *(to practise)*

Q12 Write the **simple past tense** forms of the verbs below.

a) choose	....	**g)** cut	....	**m)** break	....
b) bind	....	**h)** bend	....	**n)** freeze	....
c) fall	....	**i)** draw	....	**o)** hold	....
d) build	....	**j)** grow	....	**p)** leave	....
e) deal	....	**k)** feed	....	**q)** shake	....
f) feel	....	**l)** bleed	....	**r)** keep	....

Checking Your Spelling

Q1   Draw a clear **line** through each **misspelt word** and write the **correct** version **above** it.

     Christian Aid was set up after World War II to help refugees. It now works ~~globaly~~ *globally* to releive

poverty. It raises money through donacions, events and colections. Most of Christian Aid's work

is in developmant. Projects set up by Christian Aid focus on poor sanitacion, education and

healthcare, as well as encouraging the use of birth control. The organisation also aims to change

governmant policy to reduce the sufering of the world's poor, e.g. through debt releif.

Q2   Circle the words that are spelt **incorrectly**, and write the **correct** version in the box.

disappear	acording	beginning	maintenence	vareity
opposite	essentialy	catergory	reference	successfull

```
┌──────────────────────────────────────────────────────────────────────────┐
│                                                                            │
│                                                                            │
│                                                                            │
│                                                                            │
└──────────────────────────────────────────────────────────────────────────┘
```

Q3   Rewrite this passage and **correct** the spelling **mistakes**. Hint: there are **10** spelling errors.

    As a country becomes more developped, its population often increases. One reason is that
the medicall facilitys in the country improve, so its patients have better access to doctors and
the medecines they need. Also, life expectency increases because people have better nutritian.
However, a growing population can lead to houseing problems and rising unnemployment
because their are not sufficent jobs.

....

....

....

....

....

....

....

....

....

Checking Your Punctuation

Q1   Circle the **punctuation error** in each sentence. There is **one** error in each sentence.

   a) Air pollution and rapid urbanisation cause problems in Beijing and mumbai.

   b) During Ramadan, Muslims' fast during the daylight hours (between sunrise and sunset).

   c) The exam question asked students why the Great Depression occurred in America?

   d) Kenya's economy depends on tourism, agriculture, farming and, mining.

   e) In 'Macbeth', the country's well-being is linked to that of it's king.

   f) Tourism can benefit local industries, that supply tourist attractions or restaurants.

Q2   Add the **missing punctuation mark** to each sentence. There is **one** missing in every sentence.

   a) 'Animal Farm' , written by George Orwell is based on historical events .

   b) There were many anti war protests during the early 21st century .

   c) Think about these aspects of the poem subject , form , rhyme and rhythm .

   d) After a volcanic eruption , there is a big crater a caldera) left behind .

   e) In the 1930s , Italy and Japan both invaded other countries territories .

   f) " There are a lot of employees off sick " said the manager, " and I feel ill today . "

   g) Although the Allies won the war many British people did not celebrate .

Q3   Rewrite this passage and **correct** the **punctuation mistakes**. Hint: there are **10** errors.

   Peoples' attitudes changed as the war went on In 1914, there was enthusiasm for the war but by 1918, people were disillusioned with it? Propaganda (persuasive words or images was used to encourage men to join the army. Lord kitchener appeared on a poster with the words, Your country needs you" beside him. The government also used it's propaganda to raise the countrys morale. By the end, of 1917, most British people wanted the war to end.

   ....

   ....

   ....

   ....

   ....

   ....

   ....

   ....

Checking Your Grammar

Q1 Draw a clear **line** through each **verb** in the **wrong tense** and write the **correct** version **above** it.

Rivers flood for a variety of reasons. After a long period of rain, the soil ~~became~~ *becomes* saturated, so it is unable to take in any extra water. This means that more water ran off into the rivers and there is a higher risk of flooding. Flooding also occurred when snow and ice melt quickly, because a large quantity of water enters the river system in a very short space of time. If this coincides with a period of heavy or prolonged rainfall, the combination of factors increased the risk of flooding.

Human factors can also caused river flooding, through actions such as deforestation. Trees collected water on their leaves which then evaporates, and they draw up water through their roots, so there is less water in the ground. If there were fewer trees, the water runs off into rivers, causing them to rise.

Q2 Underline the **incorrect** word in each sentence and write the **correct** version on the line.

a) 'Pride and Prejudice' was wrote by Jane Austen and published in 1813. ....

b) Juliet drinks the potion that Friar Laurence gives hers and falls asleep. ....

c) After the rain, the water in the river were rising at an alarming rate. ....

d) Harry and me worked on a History project about Queen Victoria. ....

e) Lady Macbeth says she would of killed Duncan herself if she could. ....

f) The soul is the spiritual part of a person that ain't a physical substance. ....

Q3 Rewrite this passage and **correct** the **grammar mistakes**. There are **6** grammar errors.

At the beginning of 'Animal Farm', Old Major describes a vision he has in that the animals take over the farm and work for ourselves. He criticises Man because he doesn't do no work but he benefits from all the animals' work. Old Major want all the animals to be equal and it teaches them a song about what life was like in the future, when the animals rule themselves.

....

....

....

....

....

....

....

Proofreading

Q1 There are **spelling**, **punctuation** and **grammar errors** in each of these passages. Rewrite the passages and **correct** the mistakes. There are **14** errors in each one.

a) The UK is a democratic soceity, which mean that the british people elect representatives to run the country. In the UK, every adult citisen has the right to vote (unless they are in prison. During the 19ᵗʰ centery, sevral reform acts had gave most men the vote

However, in the early 1900s, women still couldnt' vote in national elections. People thought that women belonged at home, and it were the man's role to take part in public affairs. After many years' of protests, women finaly achieve equal voting rights to men in 1928.

....

....

....

....

....

....

....

....

b) Christians believe that they have a duty to be charitible and show love, to other people. 'Charity' means any help that is gave freely to other people. Here are some things people can give: time, such as visiting the elderly; effort, who could involve building a comunity centre; and material things, for instance, donateing money.

Some religious groups' are dedicated to releiving suffering among the poor and sick! Mother Teresa devoted herself to helping people in Calcutta, india. Her set up a religious order who's members now helped the poor all over the world

....

....

....

....

....

....

....

....

Proofreading

Q2 There are **spelling**, **punctuation** and **grammar errors** in each of these passages. Rewrite the passages and **correct** the mistakes. There are **14** errors in each one.

a) There is many features who make up spoken language! When someone speaks their accent and dialect (the way they pronounce certain words can reveal alot about our background. The situation can also effect the langauge that people uses. For example, if your'e in a restaurant, you might use set language routines, such as, "Could I have the bill, please"? Also, some people doesn't always say what they mean, so you might need to look for implyed meanings.

....

....

....

....

....

....

....

....

....

b) Food are important to many religons, especially during certain festivels. Christians Muslims and Jews all believe that God is the creater, and so ultimatly all food comes from God. One of the importantest events in the Jewish calendar is called Passover; this is a time when Jews eat speciffic foods. Yeast is forbiden, so Jews eat unleavened bread (bread made without yeast.)
Fasting (not eating for a period of time is part of many religions to. For example, muslims fast between sun-rise and sunset during the month of Ramadan.

....

....

....

....

....

....

....

....

....

Answers

Section One — Spelling

Pages 1-3 — Plurals

Q1 Plurals that add 's': version<u>s</u>, character<u>s</u>, religion<u>s</u>, conflict<u>s</u>
Plurals that add 'es': speech<u>es</u>, branch<u>es</u>, process<u>es</u>

Q2 **a)** atlas<u>es</u>, compass<u>es</u>, pupil<u>s</u>
b) taxi<u>s</u>, passenger<u>s</u>, item<u>s</u>
c) trench<u>es</u>, soldier<u>s</u>
d) box<u>es</u>, stair<u>s</u>, sock<u>s</u>
e) alliance<u>s</u>, nation<u>s</u>, idea<u>s</u>
f) church<u>es</u>, crucifix<u>es</u>, altar<u>s</u>
g) area<u>s</u>, tourist<u>s</u>, beach<u>es</u>

Q3 Plurals that should end '-ies':
nationali<u>ties</u>, du<u>ties</u>, poli<u>cies</u>, come<u>dies</u>, tenden<u>cies</u>, subtle<u>ties</u>, na<u>vies</u>.

Q4 **a)** The train crash caused <u>delays</u> to all <u>journeys</u> from Manchester.
b) Geologists carried out <u>surveys</u> on two V-shaped <u>valleys</u> in Wales.
c) Leaders of many different <u>countries</u> signed both peace <u>treaties</u>.
d) There are several <u>charities</u> which help <u>families</u> to adopt children.

Q5 **a)** studio<u>s</u>
b) echo<u>es</u>
c) ratio<u>s</u>
d) potato<u>es</u>
e) hero<u>es</u>
f) logo<u>s</u>
g) tomato<u>es</u>
h) solo<u>s</u>

Q6 During our trip to the rainforest, we took our <u>canoes</u> and paddled down two enormous rivers. We saw a whole host of different animals, including <u>butterflies</u> and flying <u>foxes</u>. In the evening, we watched some <u>monkeys</u> playing in the trees whilst we camped by the riverbank. Clara had packed everything we needed, from firelighters and sleeping bags, to cards and <u>dominoes</u> for our evening entertainment. Julie, however, had packed some silly things — she brought along two portable <u>radios</u>, and she packed her favourite dresses and her dancing shoes because she thought there would be some <u>discos</u> nearby.

Q7 **a)** thie<u>ves</u>, cliff<u>s</u>
b) midwi<u>ves</u>, li<u>ves</u>
c) chef<u>s</u>, kni<u>ves</u>
d) wol<u>ves</u>, cal<u>ves</u>

Q8 **a)** Understanding mobile phone <u>tariffs</u> can be very complicated.
b) A person's religious <u>beliefs</u> affect their behaviour.
c) Two <u>halves</u> make a whole.
d) The walls of the temple were covered with colourful <u>motifs</u>.

Q9 **a)** In 1914, Britain had around 700 000 <u>men</u> in its army.
b) Snowdon is about 3 560 <u>feet</u> high.
c) Some <u>children</u> use Advent calendars to count off the days until Christmas.
d) Before the 1960s, most of the food <u>people</u> ate was grown in the UK.
e) Students must meet several <u>criteria</u> to join the society.

Q10 **a)** <u>Women</u> gained more freedom in Britain in the 1920s.
b) There is a story in the Bible about 5 <u>loaves</u> and 2 fish.

c) In the trenches, soldiers had to live alongside rats and <u>lice</u>.
d) Turkeys or <u>geese</u> form a traditional part of the Christmas meal for many people.
e) There are two <u>Jameses</u> among Jesus's disciples.
f) The Romans and the Greeks used toothpicks to clean their <u>teeth</u>.
g) The <u>Kennedys</u> were a famous American family.

Q11 Words that stay the same in the plural are:
<u>aircraft</u>, <u>species</u>, <u>moose</u>, <u>offspring</u> and <u>salmon</u>.

Q12 Add 's' in the plural: continent<u>s</u>, officer<u>s</u>, camera<u>s</u>.
Add 'es' in the plural: witness<u>es</u>, bench<u>es</u>, sandwich<u>es</u>.
Change to 'ves' in the plural: wi<u>ves</u>, li<u>ves</u>, kni<u>ves</u>, thie<u>ves</u>.
Stay the same in the plural: <u>series</u>, <u>evidence</u>.

Pages 4-5 — Prefixes

Q1 You should have circled: un-, in-, il-, re-, ir-, fore-, dis-, pre-, mis- and mid-.
You should have underlined: known, competent, logical, trace, regular, tell, taste, date, spell and way.

Q2 **a)** <u>un</u>important
b) <u>in</u>dependent
c) <u>in</u>definite
d) <u>un</u>contested
e) <u>un</u>common
f) <u>in</u>conclusive
g) <u>un</u>intentional
h) <u>in</u>appropriate

Q3 **a)** <u>Il</u>legally parked vehicles will be removed immediately.
b) Some people thought women were too <u>ir</u>rational to have the vote.
c) It's not always possible to explain the <u>ir</u>regular results of an experiment.
d) <u>Im</u>proper use of the machinery could lead to injury.
e) If you write <u>il</u>legibly in your exam, you could lose some marks.
f) Mrs Cox sent an <u>im</u>personal letter to the head of the department.
g) The mission's success is <u>ir</u>refutable.
h) Many people in the 17th century were <u>il</u>literate.

Q4 Possible answers include:
a) <u>re</u>type, <u>mis</u>type
b) <u>pre</u>view, <u>re</u>view
c) <u>dis</u>charge, <u>re</u>charge
d) <u>re</u>active, <u>pro</u>active
e) <u>re</u>trial, <u>mis</u>trial
f) <u>pre</u>arrange, <u>re</u>arrange
g) <u>un</u>able, <u>dis</u>able
h) <u>dis</u>count, <u>mis</u>count

Q5 **a)** The Prime Minister asked for some <u>impartial</u> advice.
b) Carla's reward was <u>disproportionate</u> to the effort she had made.
c) The protesters gave an <u>impassioned</u> response to the arrival of the police.
d) <u>Overloaded</u> vehicles can be serious road hazards.
e) The audience was <u>entranced</u> by the pianist's performance.

Q6 **a)** The players' bad behaviour brought the team into <u>disrepute</u>.
b) The returning soldiers were <u>overwhelmed</u> by the enthusiastic welcome they received.

Answers

c) Due to rising sea levels, low-lying islands like the Maldives will be <u>sub</u>merged.

d) The flood victims found the town's decision to proceed with the carnival <u>in</u>considerate.

e) Some say the love between a parent and their child is <u>un</u>conditional.

f) Personal items destroyed during an earthquake are often <u>ir</u>replaceable.

g) The trenches were particularly <u>un</u>pleasant places to live.

h) Rewarding pupils for disrupting lessons would be an <u>un</u>conventional approach.

i) The offensive poster was probably put up by people wishing to <u>dis</u>credit the King.

j) <u>Under</u>ground water and sewage pipes run beneath the building's foundations.

Q7 Due to a silly <u>mis</u>understanding, Mrs Dally accidentally rented out her property to the wrong tenant. She had intended to let Adam Richards live in the flat, but instead she discovered that a man called Richard Adams was moving in. Mrs Dally was <u>un</u>sure as to how this had happened, but she suspected she'd been <u>mis</u>led.

When she discussed the matter with her new tenant, he stared at her in disbelief and claimed she was speaking <u>non</u>sense. He said it was <u>im</u>possible that such an error could have been made, and he was <u>un</u>happy that she was questioning him in this rather <u>im</u>polite manner.

Pages 6-7 — Suffixes

Q1 You should have circled:
-ed, -able, -er, -ment, -ing, -or, -ly, -ful, -less and -ence.
You should have underlined:
intend, question, wait, amend, camp, inspect, perfect, thank, motion and depend.

Q2 a) During the <u>celebration</u>, balloons and sweets were handed out to visitors.

b) The council's decision to close the library upset the entire <u>community</u>.

c) The countries formed alliances for <u>security</u> reasons.

d) Some Christians believe that vocations are meant to be <u>challenging</u>.

e) Hitler <u>persuaded</u> the Czech president to allow German troops into the country.

f) During a power cut, some businesses may rely on a back-up <u>generator</u>.

Q3 a) The outbreak of war caused destruction on an unimagin<u>able</u> scale.

b) Our trip to the Arctic Circle was a truly memor<u>able</u> experience.

c) Staying in a youth hostel is a sens<u>ible</u> way to save money on holiday.

d) You may be inelig<u>ible</u> to sit on the board of directors.

e) The company believes bullying in the workplace is not accept<u>able</u>.

f) After the fire, officials declared the house uninhabit<u>able</u>.

g) You can make up statistics in an essay, but they must be plaus<u>ible</u>.

Q4 a) demonstra<u>tion</u> **j)** segrega<u>tion</u>
b) deci<u>sion</u> **k)** discrimina<u>tion</u>
c) ten<u>sion</u> **l)** discu<u>ssion</u>
d) politi<u>cian</u> **m)** opti<u>cian</u>
e) situa<u>tion</u> **n)** congrega<u>tion</u>
f) interven<u>tion</u> **o)** revi<u>sion</u>
g) op<u>tion</u> **p)** confu<u>sion</u>
h) inva<u>sion</u> **q)** magi<u>cian</u>
i) oppre<u>ssion</u> **r)** emo<u>tion</u>

Q5 a) heav<u>ier</u> **f)** bus<u>ier</u>
b) laz<u>iest</u> **g)** apply<u>ing</u>
c) enjoy<u>able</u> **h)** haz<u>iest</u>
d) trend<u>iest</u> **i)** trick<u>ier</u>
e) dry<u>ing</u> **j)** wear<u>ing</u>

Q6

Root Word	-ing	-ful	-ed
hope	hop<u>ing</u>	hope<u>ful</u>	hop<u>ed</u>
care	car<u>ing</u>	care<u>ful</u>	car<u>ed</u>
force	forc<u>ing</u>	force<u>ful</u>	forc<u>ed</u>
doubt	doubt<u>ing</u>	doubt<u>ful</u>	doubt<u>ed</u>
taste	tast<u>ing</u>	taste<u>ful</u>	tast<u>ed</u>
dread	dread<u>ing</u>	dread<u>ful</u>	dread<u>ed</u>
respect	respect<u>ing</u>	respect<u>ful</u>	respect<u>ed</u>

Q7 a) Thousands of refugees left their homes in despera<u>tion</u>.

b) Jesus challenged his followers' views about the treat<u>ment</u> of others.

c) Many countries were respon<u>sible</u> for starting the war.

d) The Gospels are an important source of guid<u>ance</u> for Christians.

e) The country's problems should be handled with a sense of urg<u>ency</u>.

f) Roman Catholics believe in a state of exis<u>tence</u> called Purgatory.

g) Health insur<u>ance</u> pays for medical treatment.

h) There was a lot of excite<u>ment</u> about the company's new bonus scheme.

i) Juliet's actions show that she is definite<u>ly</u> not a submissive character.

Pages 8-9 — Suffixes and Double Letters

Q1 a) equi<u>pp</u>ed **d)** promo<u>ter</u>
b) regre<u>tt</u>ed **e)** master<u>ful</u>
c) forgo<u>tt</u>en **f)** eventua<u>ll</u>y

Q2 You should have ticked:
signal, refer, worship, prefer and admit.

Answers

Q3

Root Word	-ed	-ing	-ment
commit	committed	committing	commitment
amend	amended	amending	amendment
ship	shipped	shipping	shipment
attain	attained	attaining	attainment
resent	resented	resenting	resentment
enrol	enrolled	enrolling	enrolment
develop	developed	developing	development
fulfil	fulfilled	fulfilling	fulfilment
recruit	recruited	recruiting	recruitment

Q4 a) Denise claimed she was only a <u>beginner</u> and that's why she lost.
b) The prince <u>forfeited</u> his right to become King of England.
c) The government needs to start <u>controlling</u> its budget.
d) The builders <u>allotted</u> a proportion of the road to cyclists.
e) Archeologists <u>admitted</u> that the remains were not very old.
f) Racism is a <u>recurring</u> theme throughout the novel.

Q5 a) The German Mark became <u>virtually</u> <u>worthless</u>.
b) The game between Spain and Wales turned out to be a <u>goalless</u> draw.
c) Investigators believed the facts had been <u>omitted</u> from the report.
d) Each machine <u>gunner</u> was responsible for his or her own weapon.
e) In a mosque, women are not <u>permitted</u> to lead the prayers of men.
f) The resistant rock is eroded more slowly and it's left <u>jutting</u> out.

Q6 a) Rasheed <u>accidentaly</u> dropped the envelopes all over the floor.　　(accidentally)
b) Make sure your sketches are neat and clearly <u>labeled</u>.　　(labelled)
c) The arguments continued, so the meeting was <u>canceled</u>.　　(cancelled)
d) The charity was <u>commited</u> to helping the environment.　　(committed)
e) <u>Forgeting</u> traumatic experiences can be a way of coping.　　(forgetting)

Q7 Double the last letter when adding 'ing': shrivel, pedal, expel and rebel
Don't double the last letter when adding 'ing': catch, proof, demand and protest

Page 10 — Other Words With Double Letters

Q1 a) Employees are paid for every <u>suggestion</u> they make about productivity.
b) The Dr. Martin Luther King, Jr. <u>Association</u> is in San Jose, California.

c) Sam said his car cost over £50 000, but this was an <u>exaggeration</u>.
d) Reducing our carbon footprint is considered to be absolutely <u>necessary</u>.
e) Amanda and Erica were intimidated by the dog's <u>aggressive</u> behaviour.
f) The U-2 crisis caused <u>embarrassment</u> for President Eisenhower.
g) It was a momentous <u>occasion</u> when America gained independence from Britain.
h) The fun run raised over £100 000, which proves the event was a huge <u>success</u>.
i) The <u>assassination</u> of Archduke Franz Ferdinand had devastating consequences.
j) Members of the tennis <u>committee</u> decided to resurface the tennis courts.

Q2 dile<u>mm</u>a, sci<u>ss</u>ors, biza<u>rr</u>e, gra<u>ss</u>hopper, disa<u>pp</u>oint, reco<u>mm</u>end, interru<u>pt</u>, tomo<u>rr</u>ow

Q3 a) di<u>ss</u>imilar
b) disa<u>pp</u>ear
c) va<u>n</u>ish
d) di<u>ff</u>erent
e) a<u>cc</u>o<u>mm</u>odation
f) be<u>l</u>onging
g) po<u>ss</u>ession
h) addre<u>ss</u>
i) communication
j) tra<u>d</u>ition
k) transmi<u>tt</u>ing
l) commu<u>n</u>ist
m) thermo<u>m</u>eter
n) o<u>pp</u>ortunity
o) discri<u>m</u>inate
p) forbi<u>dd</u>en
q) glo<u>b</u>al
r) emi<u>ss</u>ion

Page 11 — Silent Letters

Q1 wh<u>i</u>ch, s<u>c</u>ent, gnome, shou<u>l</u>d, t<u>w</u>o, <u>wh</u>ile, <u>t</u>sar, des<u>c</u>end, wou<u>l</u>d, <u>w</u>rite, <u>w</u>rong, wom<u>b</u>, de<u>b</u>t, <u>k</u>neel, ans<u>w</u>er

Q2 a) Hayley isn't sure <u>whether</u> to go for a walk — it <u>could</u> start to rain.
b) Chalk is a <u>white</u> sedimentary rock used to make concrete.
c) In the Bible, it states that Jesus had twelve <u>disciples</u>.
d) The <u>whole</u> event was a disaster because <u>half</u> of the bands didn't turn up.
e) Police had to cordon off the crime <u>scene</u> to keep the public away.

Q3 a) The defendant denied all <u>nowledge</u> of an attempt to overthrow the <u>goverment</u>. (knowledge, government)
b) Mrs Clark was annoyed that the children <u>woudn't</u> <u>lisen</u> to her. (wouldn't, listen)
c) Historians don't <u>kno</u> <u>wether</u> the Knights of the Round Table existed or not. (know, whether)
d) Daniel finally told Ben the truth and was able to sleep with a clear <u>consience</u>. (conscience)
e) I'm just going to the <u>cemist</u> to get some medication for my <u>nee</u>. (chemist, knee)

Q4 a) s<u>c</u>ience
b) tom<u>b</u>
c) cas<u>t</u>le
d) ans<u>w</u>er
e) <u>Ch</u>ristmas

Answers

Page 12 — Unstressed Vowels

Q1 You should have ticked:
private, original, dictionary, separate, alphabet, central, primary, woman and bedlam.

Q2
a) different
b) vegetable
c) interest
d) marvellous
e) general
f) original
g) instrument
h) necessary
i) totally
j) jewellery
k) desperate
l) boundary
m) vowel
n) frighten
o) describe

Q3
a) The scientists can't explain the strange results — they're completely rand<u>o</u>m.
b) Our postm<u>a</u>n was unable to make the deliv<u>e</u>ry because he was scared of our dog.
c) There's a plaque in the town centre in mem<u>o</u>ry of fallen soldiers.
d) The USA wanted the treaty to be gen<u>e</u>rous to stop a similar war happening again.
e) Many people believe the governm<u>e</u>nt shouldn't dictate how charities spend their money.
f) Any outside interfer<u>e</u>nce will defin<u>i</u>tely have a detriment<u>a</u>l effect.

Q4 The Darvaza Gas Crater in Turkmenistan is a curious geographic<u>a</u>l phenomenon in the heart of the Karakum Desert. It is believed that the crater was created when a rig drilling for natural gas accident<u>a</u>lly fell into an underground cav<u>e</u>rn. The incid<u>e</u>nt happened in 1971 and a fire has been burning in the crater ever since. The smell of burning sulphur can be detected for quite some dist<u>a</u>nce.

Page 13 — i Before e Rule

Q1
a) Even though my friend asked for a <u>reciept</u> for her dress, she didn't get one.   (<u>receipt</u>)
b) Although Jonathan is on a diet, he has just ordered a gigantic <u>peice</u> of cake.   (<u>piece</u>)
c) When the phone rang, Caroline dashed to pick up the <u>reciever</u>.   (<u>receiver</u>)
d) It was a great <u>releif</u> to discover that the snake on my leg wasn't poisonous.   (<u>relief</u>)
e) Whilst on holiday in the Arctic, my neighbour had to camp on a <u>glaceir</u>.   (<u>glacier</u>)

Q2
a) The th<u>ie</u>f broke into the shop through the roof, making a hole in the c<u>ei</u>ling.
b) Police officers tried to s<u>ei</u>ze the armed robbers after a f<u>ie</u>rce battle in the street.
c) If you dec<u>ei</u>ve the judges, you will forf<u>ei</u>t your right to stay in the competition.
d) During the r<u>ei</u>gn of Queen Elizabeth I, many people had poor hyg<u>ie</u>ne.
e) Pupils usually learn about prot<u>ei</u>ns in sc<u>ie</u>nce lessons.
f) Fishing boats can leak oil and d<u>ie</u>sel, which harms aquatic animals.
g) Rocks can be changed by the pressure from the w<u>ei</u>ght of the material above them.

h) Sl<u>ei</u>ghs are sometimes used for transportation, especially in Arctic regions.
i) Pamela's n<u>ie</u>ce is travelling to Australia next year.
j) When the alarm sounded, a p<u>ie</u>rcing noise filled the air.
k) Food had to be rationed because there weren't suffic<u>ie</u>nt supplies to feed the nation.
l) There are several spec<u>ie</u>s of spider whose venom is poisonous to humans.

Q3
a) agenc<u>ies</u>
b) heav<u>ier</u>
c) modif<u>ied</u>
d) vacanc<u>ies</u>
e) fanc<u>ied</u>
f) den<u>ied</u>
g) juic<u>iest</u>
h) clarif<u>ied</u>

Pages 14-15 — Forming Comparatives

Q1 You should have ticked:
a) Jupiter is bigger than Earth.
b) Sofas are more comfortable than stools.
c) Health is more important than money.
d) I'm at greater risk than you are.
e) Japanese is harder than French.

Q2
a) Cycling to school is <u>better</u> than going by car.
b) The plague was <u>worse</u> than people expected.
c) Ruby has <u>less</u> money than Margaret.
d) Farmer Bob owns <u>more</u> land than Farmer Ted.

Q3
a) Africa is <u>larger than</u> Europe.
b) Fruit and vegetables are <u>healthier than</u> fried food.
c) Lakes are <u>smaller than</u> oceans.
d) Steel is <u>stronger than</u> plastic.
e) Some countries are <u>wealthier than</u> other countries.
f) Comics are usually <u>funnier than</u> magazines.

Q4
a) Runners-up are <u>less successful than</u> winners.
b) Holidays are <u>less stressful than</u> trips to the dentist.
c) Chipped antiques are <u>less valuable than</u> antiques in perfect condition.
d) Flimsy bike locks are <u>less secure than</u> heavy-duty padlocks.
e) Easy questions are <u>less challenging than</u> hard questions.

Q5
a) Melanie walks <u>as slowly as</u> a snail.
b) In summer, our greenhouse feels <u>as hot as</u> an oven.
c) King Richard I was <u>as brave as</u> a lion.

Q6
a) Mount Everest is the <u>highest</u> mountain in the world.
b) World War I was one of the <u>worst</u> wars in history.
c) Exam questions are the <u>best</u> way to practise what you've learnt.
d) Liam gave the <u>most complicated</u> answer possible.

Q7
a) clever<u>est</u>
b) <u>most</u> difficult
c) trend<u>iest</u>
d) <u>most</u> confusing
e) deep<u>est</u>
f) fast<u>est</u>
g) <u>most</u> famous
h) <u>most</u> original
i) happ<u>iest</u>
j) <u>most</u> dangerous

Q8
a) Ron is friendly, but Jim is <u>the friendliest</u> person I know.

b) Geoff's house is expensive, but Julian's is <u>the most expensive</u> house on the street.

c) Cereal is healthy, but fruit is <u>the healthiest</u> breakfast.

d) Hobbies are important, but education is <u>the most important</u> thing.

e) Zoos are fun, but theme parks are <u>the most fun</u>.

f) Granny is old, but Great-Granny is <u>the oldest</u> relative I have.

g) Claire's hair is long, but Tara's hair is <u>the longest</u> hair I've ever seen.

Pages 16-19 — Commonly Misused Words

Q1 a) Winston Churchill <u>may be</u> the most famous British Prime Minister in history.

b) Carbon dioxide emissions <u>may be</u> harming the Earth's atmosphere.

c) <u>Maybe</u> we should sail to France rather than go by plane.

d) Christianity <u>may be</u> the fastest-growing religion in the world.

e) The President's policy of high taxes was <u>maybe</u> making the situation worse.

Q2 a) Some nations aim to help war-stricken countries in <u>any way</u> they can.

b) <u>Every body</u> of experts agreed on the report's findings.

c) <u>Nobody</u> can leave the room until <u>every one</u> of those windows is closed.

d) Is <u>anybody</u> interested in going on a trip to Prestatyn?

e) The flood victims had enough support, but aid workers arrived on the scene <u>anyway</u>.

f) <u>Everybody</u> who feels ill needs to go to see the nurse immediately.

g) Life and death issues are important to <u>everyone</u>.

h) <u>Any body</u> of deep water can be dangerous.

Q3 a) To become law, a bill must <u>always</u> be approved by the monarch.

b) <u>All ways</u> of generating extra funds must be considered.

c) <u>Altogether</u>, King Henry VIII had six wives.

d) If we approach the boss <u>all together</u>, maybe she'll listen to us.

Q4 a) The toaster turned <u>into</u> a robot.

b) We went <u>in to</u> ask for directions.

c) I handed my homework <u>in to</u> Mrs Watt.

d) He had to stay <u>in to</u> do the chores.

e) The dog sneaked <u>into</u> the hairdressers.

Q5 a) Some Catholics <u>practise</u> their religion by attending Mass on a regular basis.

b) If you want to renew your <u>licence</u>, you'll have to take the test again.

c) The Prime Minister's aide was unable to give any practical <u>advice</u>.

d) It would be great if there was a <u>device</u> for controlling the weather.

e) Martin Luther King <u>advised</u> people to never lose hope.

f) Vanessa is <u>licensed</u> to drive heavy goods vehicles.

g) Many religious <u>practices</u> were banned in the Soviet Union.

h) We need to <u>devise</u> a cunning plan to outsmart the enemy.

Q6 a) Parliament <u>passed</u> the Abolition of Death Penalty Act in 1965.

b) The <u>effects</u> of the Hiroshima and Nagasaki bombings can still be seen today.

c) The speeding driver had to <u>accept</u> the consequences of his actions.

d) Cliffs formed from soft rock or <u>loose</u> material can retreat quickly.

e) The River Rhine runs <u>past</u> Cologne, Bonn and Koblenz.

f) All the inventions, <u>except</u> the chocolate teapot, were awarded a prize.

g) If shareholders <u>lose</u> confidence, they may sell their shares.

h) Evacuation <u>affected</u> thousands of children during the war.

Q7 Dear Gareth,

<u>Thankyou</u> so much for the wonderful birthday present. It's the best gift I've received in a long time. <u>Infact</u>, I would go so far as to say it's the best present I've ever been given. It would be great to hear from you soon — I've enclosed a note with my address on it <u>incase</u> you've forgotten it.

Once again, thanks <u>alot</u>.

Michael

(thank you, in fact, in case, a lot)

The mistakes are written as one word; the correct spellings are written as <u>two</u> words.

Q8 <u>There</u> are many reasons why people decide to change <u>their</u> religion. Some people choose to convert due to a change in <u>their</u> beliefs. Others might be forced to follow a different faith by a totalitarian regime controlling <u>their</u> country. In this case, citizens might feel as though <u>they're</u> putting <u>their</u> lives at risk if they don't agree to convert to a new religion.

Q9 a) Soldiers usually <u>wear</u> camouflaged uniforms so they blend in with their environment.

b) If we take a compass, we should be able to work out <u>where</u> we are.

c) When we finally arrived at the summit, we <u>were</u> ready for a long rest.

Q10 a) After the war, the main powers found they had spent <u>too</u> much money on the war.

b) The next planned mission <u>to</u> Mars has been postponed until further notice.

c) Plates are made of <u>two</u> types of crust — continental and oceanic.

d) If someone embraces Islam later in life, he or she is said <u>to</u> be 'returning'.

e) Although deforestation has some positive impacts, it has quite a lot of negative ones <u>too</u>.

Q11 a) The field <u>of</u> science is fascinating and complex.

b) During air raids, street lights were switched <u>off</u>.

c) Oceans cover roughly 71 per cent <u>of</u> the Earth's surface.

Answers

d) The shoe shop's sale sign says, "All boots 80% <u>off</u>".

Q12 a) Judaism teaches that we should look after those who <u>are</u> less fortunate than ourselves.

b) Fair elections and the right to peaceful protest <u>are</u> vital parts of <u>our</u> society.

c) Some people believe <u>our</u> existence is a test to see if we <u>are</u> fit for Heaven.

Q13 a) <u>Though</u> the 1920s had been a 'boom time', there were economic problems.

b) If you present a <u>thorough</u> analysis of the facts, you'll do well in the exam.

c) The German troops went <u>through</u> Belgium to attack France.

d) The Prime Minister raised taxes even <u>though</u> it was unpopular.

e) In the 17th century, many people <u>thought</u> that the Earth was flat.

f) The <u>thorough</u> reshuffling of the cabinet caused some ministers to lose their jobs.

g) Tunnels have been drilled <u>through</u> some fold mountains to make straight roads.

h) The report was a <u>thorough</u> investigation into the business's problems.

i) Magma rises <u>through</u> cracks in the Earth's crust.

j) For many believers, Heaven is a comforting <u>thought</u>.

Q14 a) Some citizens were worried that joining the League of Nations could cost <u>them</u> money.

b) Jairus was a synagogue ruler whose daughter was <u>brought</u> back to life by Jesus.

c) The Cuban Missile Crisis of 1962 <u>brought</u> the world to the brink of nuclear war.

d) The aid may not reach <u>those</u> who need it because of things like transport problems.

e) People had to use rationing coupons when they <u>bought</u> butter, sugar and meat.

f) Indoctrinating pupils was aimed to make <u>them</u> less likely to resist Nazi control.

g) The reward for <u>those</u> who have followed Allah will be entry into Paradise.

h) High order goods, such as washing machines, are only <u>bought</u> occasionally.

i) King Duncan is praised for rewarding <u>those</u> who are loyal to him.

Q15 a) Training schemes help people to <u>learn</u> new skills.

b) Most religions <u>teach</u> that we all move on to an afterlife.

c) The Dawes Plan meant the US would <u>lend</u> money to Germany.

d) Very poor countries <u>borrow</u> money from other countries.

Pages 20-21 — Other Tricky Words

Q1 a) re<u>c</u>ommend
b) temp<u>o</u>rary
c) defin<u>i</u>tely
d) unfortun<u>a</u>tely
e) analy<u>se</u>
f) relev<u>a</u>nt
g) prob<u>a</u>bly
h) su<u>cc</u>ess
i) separate
j) opin<u>i</u>on
k) reference
l) inter<u>e</u>sting

Q2 a) The first part of President Truman's speech was a strong criti<u>c</u>ism of Communism.

b) Cardinals are respon<u>s</u>ible for electing the Pope's successor.

c) People from rural areas sometimes bel<u>ie</u>ve that the standard of living is better in cities.

d) The photo aimed to pers<u>ua</u>de German people that Hitler was a good leader.

e) Criminals who commit crimes in the heat of the moment don't think about the conse<u>q</u>uences.

f) The source has been written to exa<u>gg</u>erate the importance of Stalin.

Q3 a) The negative impacts of tourism may not be immediately <u>apparant</u>.
(apparent)

b) Headlands are usually made of resistant rocks that have <u>weakneses</u> like cracks.
(weaknesses)

c) Governments <u>deside</u> how taxes are spent, and how much is collected.
(decide)

d) There are many <u>arguements</u> both for and against the abolition of capital punishment.
(arguments)

e) Once the farmers have been taught the new <u>tecnique</u>, they'll be able to carry on using it.
(technique)

f) The country voted in favour of <u>indapendence</u>.
(independence)

g) The close contour lines on the map are <u>evidance</u> of a waterfall.
(evidence)

h) The army was poorly organised; many officers were inexperienced and <u>disipline</u> was poor.
(discipline)

i) Jews believe that God's <u>inteligance</u> is vastly higher than ours.
(intelligence)

Q4 a) su<u>cc</u>essful
b) bec<u>au</u>se
c) simil<u>a</u>r
d) nece<u>ss</u>ary
e) exp<u>e</u>rience
f) basica<u>ll</u>y
g) strength
h) s<u>c</u>hedule
i) le<u>i</u>sure
j) lib<u>r</u>ary
k) o<u>cc</u>urrence
l) rh<u>y</u>me

Q5 a) remember
b) perman<u>e</u>nt
c) conclu<u>s</u>ion
d) for<u>e</u>ign
e) <u>g</u>uard
f) ac<u>q</u>uire
g) equi<u>p</u>ment
h) medi<u>e</u>val
i) relev<u>a</u>nt
j) vacu<u>u</u>m

Q6 a) Bus <u>priority</u> lanes speed up bus services.

b) Quakers are <u>particularly</u> likely to oppose hunting.

c) Romeo kills Tybalt and is <u>consequently</u> banished.

d) Plans for <u>development</u> will generate more jobs.

e) Cheating in exams is not <u>acceptable</u>.

Q7 a) Mother Teresa won the Nobel <u>Peace</u> Prize in 1979.

b) Weak earthquakes happen <u>quite</u> often, but strong earthquakes are rare.

c) Vehicles can cause pollution even when they are <u>stationary</u>.

Answers

Pages 22-25 — Mixed Practice

Q1 a) Some Christians reject scientific <u>theories</u> on evolution.
b) Glaciers are masses of ice that fill <u>valleys</u>.
c) Some people believe that <u>miracles</u> in religious texts are metaphors.
d) The Five Pillars of Islam provide <u>opportunities</u> to know Allah.
e) The priest gave a short sermon about Christian <u>beliefs</u>.
f) For <u>centuries</u>, the finest work of leading artists was made for churches.
g) <u>Volcanoes</u> are a source of geothermal energy.
h) <u>Sheep</u> and goats are sacrificed at the Eid ul-Adha festival.
i) A severe flood could make entire <u>communities</u> homeless.

Q2

Word	Opposite
usual	<u>un</u>usual
consistency	<u>in</u>consistency
legal	<u>il</u>legal
counted	<u>dis</u>counted

Word	Opposite
confident	<u>un</u>confident
sustainable	<u>un</u>sustainable
rational	<u>ir</u>rational
understood	<u>mis</u>understood

Q3 a) The conductor stands at the front of the orchestra, facing the <u>musicians</u>.
b) Stalin controlled all information <u>available</u> to the Russian people.
c) In a river, the <u>heaviest</u> material is deposited closest to the river channel.
d) Traffic congestion and <u>pollution</u> are higher in cities.
e) The American Dream made people think that anyone could be <u>successful</u>.
f) In the Bible, Job endures <u>terrible</u> suffering and he questions God.
g) Sceptics argue that religious experiences are just <u>illusions</u>.
h) Some countries couldn't understand why nobody stood up to Hitler <u>earlier</u>.

Q4 a) trave<u>lled</u>, trave<u>lling</u>
b) pump<u>ed</u>, pump<u>ing</u>
c) benefi<u>tted</u>, benefi<u>tting</u>
d) cance<u>lled</u>, cance<u>lling</u>
e) prefe<u>rred</u>, prefe<u>rring</u>
f) tra<u>pped</u>, tra<u>pping</u>
g) di<u>pped</u>, di<u>pping</u>
h) no<u>dded</u>, no<u>dding</u>
i) offer<u>ed</u>, offer<u>ing</u>
j) ta<u>pped</u>, ta<u>pping</u>

Q5 You should have circled: secretery, aceleration, yestarday, recesion, biscit, freedem and ceramony.
The correct spellings are: secret<u>a</u>ry, a<u>c</u>celeration, yester<u>d</u>ay, rece<u>ss</u>ion, bisc<u>u</u>it, freed<u>o</u>m and cere<u>m</u>ony.

Q6 a) The farmer tried to keep the cows in th<u>eir</u> f<u>ie</u>ld.
b) I bel<u>ie</u>ve the ch<u>ie</u>f problem in our soc<u>ie</u>ty is homelessness.
c) There are several agenc<u>ie</u>s that help people to lose w<u>ei</u>ght.
d) Dec<u>ei</u>t is a prominent theme in Shakespeare's 'Macbeth'.
e) The ju<u>icie</u>st oranges come from Spain.
f) N<u>ei</u>ther side was willing to admit defeat.

Q7 a) Jonah was <u>more upset than</u> Paul when pay cuts were announced.
b) Bulk buying can be <u>cheaper than</u> making individual purchases.
c) A sand beach is <u>flatter than</u> a shingle beach.
d) The first candidates were <u>more positive than</u> the second lot of candidates.
e) Broadsheet newspapers are usually <u>more serious than</u> the tabloid press.
f) Winter evenings are <u>darker than</u> summer evenings.

Q8 a) <u>most</u> regular
b) lat<u>est</u>
c) <u>most</u> creative
d) clos<u>est</u>
e) <u>least</u>
f) <u>most</u> popular
g) <u>most</u> painful
h) <u>most</u> terrible
i) luck<u>iest</u>
j) friendl<u>iest</u>

Q9 a) Businesses <u>may be</u> set up to cater for the tourists, e.g. souvenir shops or hotels.
b) Voting is secret so no one can be pressured <u>into</u> voting for one particular candidate.
c) The politicians couldn't see <u>any way</u> of getting the bill through Parliament.
d) Not <u>everybody</u> has access to services like healthcare and education.
e) Winds <u>always</u> blow from areas of high pressure to areas of low pressure.
f) Most drugs <u>affect</u> people's judgement, so they are more likely to take risks.
g) Businesses can be damaged by floods, so people can <u>lose</u> their income.
h) It's difficult to say that <u>any one</u> reason is the main reason for Hitler's rise.
i) In 1975, the Sex Discrimination Act was <u>passed</u> by Parliament.

Q10 a) Mercutio curses the <u>two</u> feuding families.
b) During worship, Jewish men often <u>wear</u> special clothing.
c) Christians try to help <u>those</u> who need it.
d) King Duncan's sons fear for <u>their</u> lives.
e) Parents may <u>teach</u> their children to show forgiveness.
f) Romeo hates the <u>thought</u> <u>of</u> living without Juliet.

Q11 You should have circled: acomodate, completly, whereever, pavillion, collegue and tommorow.
The correct spellings are: a<u>cc</u>ommodate, complet<u>e</u>ly, wher<u>e</u>ver, pavi<u>l</u>ion, colle<u>a</u>gue and to<u>mo</u>rrow.

Q12 a) Elected commi<u>tt</u>ees of workers, peasants and soldiers were set up in 1905.
b) Military perso<u>nn</u>el entered the village to support the civilians.
c) Squatter settlements often govern themselves more su<u>cc</u>essfully than you might expect.
d) Life was begi<u>nn</u>ing to look better for Germany thanks to the work of Stresemann.
e) In the exam, use specialist vocabul<u>a</u>ry where appropriate.
f) A war may be considered just if it frees people from tyra<u>nn</u>y.
g) Preparation doesn't guarant<u>ee</u> safety from a flood.

Answers

Q13

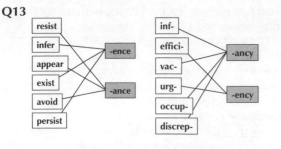

Section Two — Punctuation

Pages 26-27 — Sentence Punctuation

Q1 You should have ticked: **b)** and **c)**

Q2 a) The European Union has introduced new laws.
   b) England used to be ruled by a Danish king.
   c) Meera Syal wrote 'Anita and Me'.
   d) Christians celebrate Easter and Christmas.
   e) Lenin fled to Finland after the Bolsheviks were defeated.

Q3 a) The American stock market crashed in 1929.
   b) Did women have the right to vote in 1930?
   c) He was wondering which was the highest mountain in Europe.
   d) Lady Macbeth is an interesting character.
   e) I loved the performance of 'Lord of the Flies'; it was brilliant!
   f) Who did the Nazis blame for the 1933 Reichstag fire?
   g) She ran out of her last exam and cried, "It's over!"
   h) Destructive waves cause coastlines to erode.

Q4 a) Honduras was badly affected by _Hurricane_ Mitch in 1998.
   b) Victor Frankenstein is a _scientist_ with an obsessive desire for knowledge.
   c) General Nivelle was a French officer during _World War One_.
   d) Russia was ruled by _tsars_ until Nicholas II abdicated.
   e) The _League of Nations_ was the idea of Woodrow Wilson.
   f) Many Christians go to church on _Sundays_.
   g) There are often endangered species in _national parks_.

Q5 England is a country which has clear seasons. Winter, which runs from December to February, has colder temperatures and fewer hours of daylight. There may even be snow during winter in England. In contrast, the summer months (June to August) see higher temperatures and longer hours of daylight.
   Cambodia has very different seasons to England. The temperatures throughout the year remain high, and hours of daylight are mostly constant. Instead, Cambodia has clear wet and dry seasons. November to April are relatively dry, while monsoons from May to October bring high rainfall.

Pages 28-30 — Commas

Q1 a) Edward Rochester, Mrs Reed, Helen Burns and Blanche Ingram are four of the characters in 'Jane Eyre'.

b) India, China, Thailand and Pakistan are all situated in Asia.
   c) Sedimentary, igneous and metamorphic are the three types of rock.
   d) The Treaty of Versailles was signed by Germany, France, Britain and the USA.
   e) Victor brings a destructive, menacing creature to life.
   f) Women still worked in low-skilled, low-paid jobs in the 1920s.
   g) Macbeth is a brave, ambitious soldier.

Q2 a) Mussolini ruled Italy, but he was overthrown in 1943.
   b) Read the source, and think about the facts you know.
   c) Some Christians pray to saints, but not all do.
   d) Magwitch is a criminal, yet Pip feels sorry for him.

Q3 You should have put a cross next to: **b)**, **c)** and **e)**
   The corrected sentences should be:
   b) They watched a long, boring film.
   c) It was a dark, rainy day.
   e) It was a cold, calculated decision.

Q4 a) The Torah, the Jewish holy book, gives followers advice about how to live.
   b) Winston Churchill, a British Prime Minister, was succeeded by Clement Attlee.
   c) Mallorca, one of the Spanish Balearic islands, is a popular tourist destination.
   d) Catholicism, a denomination of Christianity, does not permit divorce.
   e) In Russia, the Kulaks, richer peasants, were resented for their wealth.
   f) The Rhône Glacier, situated in the Swiss Alps, is about 7.8 km long.

Q5 a) Benvolio, Romeo's cousin, tries to cheer Romeo up.
   b) Trevor Huddleston, an English bishop, campaigned against apartheid.
   c) The Suez Canal, an important trade route, runs through Egypt.
   d) Deforestation, the removal of trees, leads to soil erosion.
   e) 'Animal Farm', a short novel, was published in 1945.

Q6 a) Although earthly life is short, Muslims still believe it is very important.
   b) While the men were at war, women had to take on jobs at home.
   c) After the book was published, the author became famous.
   d) Although the Allies won World War One, there was little celebration.
   e) Before you write an essay, you need to write a rough plan.
   f) When a river floods onto a flood plain, the water slows down.
   g) If you have time, go back and check your work.
   h) Since God is invisible, Jews use symbols to help them focus on God in private prayer and in communal worship.

Q7 You should have ticked: **b)**, **d)** and **f)**.
   You should have put a cross next to: **a)**, **c)** and **e)**.
   The corrected sentences should read:
   a) Lydia, the youngest Bennet sister, elopes with George Wickham.

Answers

c) Islam, Christianity and Judaism all teach that there is only one god.

e) As the novel progresses, the boys descend into savagery.

Q8 'Romeo and Juliet' is a play about love, fate and conflict. It's set in the Italian city of Verona, and it tells the story of two young lovers.

At the start of the play, the Capulet and Montague families are engaged in a bitter, bloody conflict. When Romeo and Juliet, who are members of the warring families, fall in love, they know that it will be difficult for them to be together.

Friar Laurence agrees to help them marry, arranging for Juliet to fake her own death. This would allow her to run away with Romeo. However, his plan goes tragically wrong, and both lovers die needlessly at the end of the play.

Q9 After World War One, Britain, France and the USA made Germany sign a treaty. The treaty, which imposed harsh punishments, was unpopular in Germany.

Page 31 — Colons

Q1 a) There are many examples of religious charities: Christian Aid, Islamic Relief, Tearfund, World Jewish Relief and CAFOD.

b) The hydrological cycle has three parts: the sea, the land and the atmosphere.

c) Miss Havisham can be described in two words: eccentric and hateful.

d) America had several allies during the Second World War: Britain, France, China, New Zealand, Australia, Canada and the Soviet Union.

e) There are five Bennet sisters: Jane, Elizabeth, Mary, Kitty and Lydia.

f) The 20th century saw the rise of numerous European dictators: Hitler, Mussolini, Franco and several others.

g) World War Two brought several new policies: evacuation, rationing and censorship.

h) These are the key themes in 'Romeo and Juliet': love, conflict and fate.

i) Droughts have several secondary impacts: soil erosion, food shortages, unemployment and wildfires.

Q2 You should have ticked: **a)**, **b)**, **e)**, **f)** and **h)**.
You should have put a cross next to: **c)**, **d)**, **g)**, and **i)**.
The corrected sentences should read:

c) Granite is impermeable: it does not let water through.

d) The play is a tragedy: it ends with the protagonist's downfall.

g) Darcy rejects Elizabeth: he says that she is not pretty enough.

i) Fred is the opposite of Scrooge: he is cheerful and optimistic.

Page 32 — Semicolons

Q1 You should have ticked: **c)** and **e)**.
You should have put a cross next to: **a)**, **b)** and **d)**.

Q2 a) Christians believe in Heaven and Hell; Jews believe in Gan Eden and Gehinnom.

b) Muslim parents often arrange marriages for their children; they also have a responsibility to help out if the marriage begins to go wrong.

c) Climate change will affect the crops that farmers are able to grow; certain habitats may also be destroyed.

d) Planning your essay means that you can organise your ideas; leaving time to read over your work gives you the chance to spot silly errors.

e) Shield volcanoes have runny lava; dome volcanoes have thicker lava.

f) The British lost 14 ships in the battle; the Germans lost 11 ships.

Q3 a) Important Jewish festivals include Yom Kippur, which takes ten days after Jewish New Year; Pesach, or Passover, which commemorates the night of the Exodus from Egypt; and Hannukah, which celebrates the story of a day's worth of oil burning for eight days during the rededication ceremony for the Temple of Jerusalem.

b) There are several different types of nouns: proper nouns, which are the names of particular people, places or things; common nouns, which name kinds of things; collective nouns, which name groups of things; and abstract nouns, which name ideas.

c) The USA failed to defeat the communists in South Vietnam for several reasons: the American troops, most of whom were very young, were not used to fighting in the jungle; the Vietcong, the South Vietnamese communist soldiers, were very skilled in guerilla warfare; and public support for the war in the USA was decreasing.

d) Weather conditions can be tested using a thermometer to measure the temperature; a barometer to measure the air pressure, and whether it's rising or falling; a wind vane to determine the direction the wind is blowing; and an anemometer to measure the wind speed.

Page 33 — Colons and Semicolons

Q1 a) In 1900, there were five main rival nations in Europe: Britain, France, Russia, Austria-Hungary and Germany.

b) Shakespeare emphasises the status of some characters through their language: they speak in verse.

c) Christians believe in the idea of stewardship: the responsibility of humans to look after God's creation.

d) There are different types of ecosystems in the world, such as the hot, dry deserts; the hot, wet tropical rainforests; and the mild, wet climates where temperate deciduous forests are found.

e) There are several themes in 'Animal Farm': power, language, class and education.

f) Stalin died in 1953; he'd been the USSR's leader since the 1920s.

g) Jews worship in a synagogue; Muslims worship in a mosque.

Answers

Q2 **a)** Jews practise Tzedakah: the donation of 10% of their wealth to the poorest in society.

b) Earthquakes can have secondary impacts: water shortages, gas leaks and landslides.

c) The novel has several main characters: Ralph, the boys' elected leader; Jack, who rebels against Ralph; Piggy, an overweight, intelligent outsider; and Simon, who is kind, shy and spiritual.

d) ✔

Page 34 — Brackets

Q1 **a)** Christians believe that God sacrificed Jesus (his son) to forgive the sins of mankind.

b) The Inspector announces the death of Arthur's ex-employee (Eva Smith) in Act One.

c) In 1923, France invaded and occupied an industrial region of Germany (the Ruhr).

d) In Antarctica, summer (December-February) temperatures are generally close to freezing.

e) Most Hindus worship at home, but some also visit a mandir (Hindu temple).

f) Mussolini (head of the Italian Fascist Party) became Prime Minister in 1922.

g) The average summer temperature in the UK (about 14°C) is lower than mainland Europe.

h) In 'Great Expectations', Magwitch (a convict) is revealed as Pip's secret benefactor.

Q2 **a)** Islam is a monotheistic religion (followers only believe in one god).

b) The Berlin Wall (built in 1961) divided Germany in two.

c) Received pronunciation (RP) is a type of accent.

d) Supervolcanoes form over hotspots (really hot areas of mantle).

e) 'Extensive' (an adjective) means 'thorough' or 'large'.

f) TNCs (Trans-National Corporations) create jobs in an area.

Q3 World War One was fought between the Triple Alliance (Germany, Austria-Hungary and Italy) and the Triple Entente (France, Britain and Russia). Tensions between the two alliances exploded after the assassination of Archduke Franz Ferdinand (an Austro-Hungarian aristocrat) by a Serbian in 1914.

Page 35 — Hyphens

Q1 **a)** When the February Revolution came, Lenin left Switzerland and re-entered Russia.

b) Many people show their desire for peace by attending anti-war protests.

c) The Earth's mantle is made up of semi-molten rock.

d) It's useful to re-read a comprehension text before answering the questions.

e) The War Department created anti-German propaganda.

f) The edge of a cliff can eventually disappear if the rock is heavily weathered.

g) Political parties are usually made up of like-minded people.

h) Large-scale commercial farming contributes to deforestation in the Amazon.

Q2 **a)** semi-interested

b) re-educate

c) ex-President

d) pro-communist

e) unprepared

f) anti-Nazi

g) underestimate

h) self-absorbed

Q3 **a)** I got the chair back.

b) He signed something again.

c) The town is not well-known.

d) four children that are a year old

e) the improved parliament

Pages 36-37 — Apostrophes and Missing Letters

Q1 **a)** they're

b) We're

c) can't

d) shouldn't

e) don't

f) couldn't

g) I'd

h) he'd

i) who's

Q2

Long Word	Shortened Word	Long Word	Shortened Word
does not	**doesn't**	I have	**I've**
will not	**won't**	who would	**who'd**
they have	**they've**	let us	**let's**
I am	**I'm**	I had	**I'd**

Q3 **a)** The Lake District is a national park _that's_ home to deer and red squirrels.

b) The Cratchits _haven't_ got much money, but they love one another.

c) In Judaism, _there's_ a strong emphasis on moral behaviour in this life.

d) Soldiers _who'd_ survived the war were disillusioned when they returned home.

e) On the Sabbath, Jews _aren't_ supposed to do any work.

f) Without funds, the union _wasn't_ in a position to threaten new strikes.

g) Buildings can be strengthened so that _they're_ more resistant to earthquakes.

Q4 **a)** _England's_ bordered by Wales and Scotland.

b) The Bible teaches that Christians _shouldn't_ be selfish with their wealth.

c) The USSR _couldn't_ afford to keep building up its nuclear arsenal.

d) Most people _don't_ feel earthquakes of magnitude 1-2 on the Richter scale.

e) Estella rejects Pip _who's_ kind and loving towards her.

f) _Tourism's_ a growing industry — people are having more, longer holidays.

g) _There's_ a destructive plate margin along the coast of Indonesia.

Q5 **a)** Britain couldn't send supplies by sea to its troops abroad.

b) Soil erosion happens when there's heavy rainfall.

c) Buildings can be put on stilts so they're safe from floods.

d) Mr Darcy doesn't let Miss Bingley's compliments affect him.

Answers

e) <u>Photos</u> can be useful sources when <u>you're</u> studying the past.

f) The <u>boys</u> are convinced that <u>there's</u> a beast on the island.

Q6 a) lets
b) let's
c) Let's
d) lets
e) lets

Pages 38-39 — Possessive Apostrophes

Q1 b) Hyde's cane
c) Victor's invention
d) France's borders
e) a Hindu's beliefs
f) Mrs Lyons's son
g) an area's wildlife
h) the couple's wedding vows

Q2 a) Regular prayer keeps Allah in a <u>Muslim's</u> mind.
b) The <u>world's</u> longest river is the Nile.
c) The <u>country's</u> capital is New Delhi.
d) A <u>river's</u> depth is affected by rainfall.
e) The <u>region's</u> main industry is tourism.
f) The <u>character's</u> childhood is troubled and lonely.
g) By 1933, 83% of the US stock <u>market's</u> value had been lost.
h) The <u>women's</u> aim was to have the same voting rights as men.
i) A <u>religion's</u> teachings can be interpreted in different ways.
j) The <u>novel's</u> characters are often ignorant or prejudiced.

Q3 a) more than one
b) one
c) more than one
d) more than one
e) more than one
f) one
g) one
h) one
i) more than one

Q4 a) the <u>Johnstones'</u> house
b) the <u>workers'</u> struggle
c) the <u>women's</u> protest
d) the <u>mice's</u> cheese
e) the <u>girls'</u> adventure
f) the <u>children's</u> books

Q5 a) The <u>rainforest's</u> ecosystem is very fragile.
b) The <u>sisters'</u> mother is a seamstress.
c) The war went against the <u>countries'</u> agreement.
d) Newspapers criticised the <u>suffragettes'</u> violent actions.
e) A <u>believer's</u> faith can be tested when bad things happen.
f) Extreme weather can affect a <u>farmer's</u> livelihood.

Q6 b) the <u>fears</u> of the <u>characters</u>
c) the <u>decisions</u> of the <u>ministers</u>
d) the <u>themes</u> of the <u>book</u>
e) the <u>size</u> of the <u>glacier</u>
f) the <u>schools</u> of the <u>city</u>
g) the <u>reliability</u> of the <u>sources</u>
h) the <u>scenes</u> of the <u>play</u>
i) the <u>letters</u> of the <u>soldier</u>

Pages 40-41 — Its and It's

Q1 a) it has
b) it has
c) it is
d) It has
e) it is
f) it is

Q2 a) Chamonix is in eastern France; <u>*it's*</u> a popular skiing resort.
b) 'Animal Farm' is an allegory: <u>*it's*</u> based on real events.
c) During hyperinflation, money lost <u>*its*</u> value very quickly.
d) Alcohol was illegal during prohibition, but many gangs were involved in <u>*its*</u> distribution.
e) Map skills are useful, so <u>*it's*</u> worth practising them.
f) The Earth's population is increasing; <u>*it's*</u> more than doubled in the last 50 years.
g) Love is a central theme in the play, but <u>*its*</u> other themes include conflict and fate.
h) Polar ice is melting and <u>*it's*</u> causing sea levels to rise.

Q3 a) false
b) true
c) false
d) true

Q4 a) <u>It's</u> a good idea to learn the novel's plot well.
b) ✔
c) <u>It's</u> agreed that the campaign achieved many of its aims.
d) ✔
e) The UK is known for <u>its</u> countryside and <u>its</u> landmarks.
f) <u>It's</u> our responsibility to care for the planet and <u>its</u> resources.
g) <u>It's</u> important to understand poverty and its causes.

Q5 a) A synagogue often has symbols on <u>its</u> outside walls.
b) The text uses images to give <u>its</u> reader extra information.
c) A ribbon lake is usually long, and <u>it's</u> often very thin.
d) Germany attempted to double the size of <u>its</u> navy between 1900 and 1914.
e) Robert tells his sister about Victor's experiment and <u>it's</u> a chilling tale.
f) Unilateral disarmament is where just one country gives up <u>its</u> weapons.
g) If a forest is going to be used in the long term, <u>it's</u> got to be managed in a sustainable way.
h) Agnostics believe <u>it's</u> impossible to know if there's a god or not.
i) The outer layer of the Earth is the crust; <u>it's</u> very thin.
j) Pip goes to Satis House and meets <u>its</u> inhabitants.
k) A source can be useful, but it will also have <u>its</u> limitations.

Pages 42-44 — Speech Marks

Q1 a) <u>"</u>After the Cold War, the USA was the only superpower,<u>"</u> she said.
b) <u>"</u>Today we'll be talking about forgiveness,<u>"</u> said the priest.
c) She said, <u>"</u>The novel has an open ending.<u>"</u>
d) <u>"</u>There were many factors that led to the Iraq war,<u>"</u> said Emily.

Answers

e) "Many people are concerned about animal rights," he explained.

f) At the end of the show, the crowd cried, "Encore!"

g) "Evil and suffering are sent to test us," said the imam.

h) I asked, "What is the US president's name?"

i) "Shut up," said Ralph absently.

j) Mary asked, "In which continent is Iran?"

k) "Read to the end of the chapter," said Miss Phillips.

l) Clive said, "Don't believe everything you read!"

Q2 a) true   d) false
b) true   e) true
c) false

Q3 a) He said, "The river discharge tells us how much water flows in the river."

b) Jane said, "Zakah is the third Pillar of Islam."

c) "Comrades!" shouted the Major.

d) "Look at me," said Miss Havisham.

e) "When did the Second World War end?" asked Claire.

f) Did they say, "The ice is melting"?

g) "The Sabbath is a day of rest for animals as well as people," I said.

h) "Has anybody got a copy of the text?" asked Raj.

i) Jo said, "I'm drawing a timeline of the important events during the war."

Q4 You should have ticked: **a)**, **d)** and **g)**
You should have crossed: **b)**, **c)**, **e)**, **f)** and **h)**
The correct sentences are:

b) Ross said, "The hills are covered with snow."

c) Esther asked, "Will you be at the party?"

e) She said, "You can take a shortcut to work."

f) "The mouse ate the cheese," I said.

h) Kieran shouted, "Stop that thief!"

Q5 "Everybody stand up!" shouted General McGuire as he entered the canteen.
"Why should we? We've only just sat down," grumbled Lieutenant Snape.
"Don't question the General!" bellowed Colonel Jones.
"I'll tell you why. Someone has taken an extra helping," McGuire continued.
"And we're going to find out who it was!" exclaimed Jones.
"Turn out your pockets and hold out your hands," said McGuire.
"My trousers don't have pockets," said Snape.
"Roll up your trouser legs instead," replied McGuire.
"What's that?" asked Jones as he pointed to Snape's knobbly ankles.
"Apples stuffed inside his socks!" shouted McGuire.

Q6 a) "What are we studying today?" asked Beth.

b) "There is no other option," the policeman explained.

c) "Poverty leads to great suffering," said Steve.

d) "This has gone on long enough!" shouted Joanne.

Q7 I asked Tom if he would listen to my presentation on glacial landforms. He said, "Okay, but I haven't got long."
When I'd finished, Tom had lots of questions. He asked, "Why do tarns sometimes form in corries?"

"A corrie is a circular depression in the land, so water collects there to form a tarn," I explained.
He also wanted to know some examples of ribbon lakes. I said, "There are many ribbon lakes, including Windermere in the Lake District."

Page 45 — Quoting

Q1 According to the article, the people of Bridgeton have a "new passion": they are becoming "fascinated by bird-watching". The article suggests that the main reason for this was a "beautiful photograph of the common sparrow" by a local wildlife photographer.
We are also told that this popular hobby has resulted in plans for "bird boxes and a bird-watching hut" to be built locally.

Q2 Friar Laurence challenges Romeo about how quickly he has moved on from his previous love, Rosaline. He says that he can still hear Romeo's "old groans", and suggests that Romeo's tears for Rosaline are still visible: "upon thy cheek the stain doth sit / Of an old tear". He is trying to remind Romeo of all of his previous "woes".

Pages 46-49 — Mixed Practice

Q1 a) George Orwell wrote 'Animal Farm'.

b) The USA wanted to protect Vietnam.

c) Romeo and Juliet asked Friar Laurence for help.

d) Christians believe that God created the world.

e) What is the purpose of life?

f) Mount Everest is in the Himalayas.

Q2 a) Tsunamis (large sea waves) can be caused by an earthquake or volcanic eruption.

b) Gender roles (how men and women should behave) are explained in the play.

c) The Weimar Republic was established when Friedrich Ebert came to power (1919).

d) The nativity story (the story of Jesus's birth) is told in the Bible.

e) The soil on the island is shallow (about 20 cm deep).

f) Make a range of points in your essay (one per paragraph).

Q3 a) Tourists can bring more traffic to an area, which increases pollution.

b) Great Britain, France, Italy and Spain are all part of Europe.

c) 'Pride and Prejudice', written by Jane Austen, was published in 1813.

d) The end of Ramadan, the Muslim month of fasting, is marked by Eid ul-Fitr.

e) Although it takes time, make sure you check your essay for errors.

Q4 a) A nuclear family consists of parents and children; an extended family includes members of three or more generations.

b) Allah sent many prophets to guide mankind; Muhammad was the final prophet.

c) The Munich Agreement was signed in 1938; many British people supported the treaty.

d) Boxer is a principled character; he's also the hardest-working animal on the farm.

Answers

e) Earthquakes can result in people being trapped in their homes; aftershocks can sometimes make rescue attempts difficult.

f) Life in the trenches was very dangerous; many soldiers died or were wounded there.

Q5 a) New jobs were created: the economy was improving.

b) The boys can do what they like: there are no adults.

c) ✔

d) A volcanic eruption can be disastrous: the lava is dangerous.

e) ✔

f) People were not treated equally: prejudice was widespread.

Q6 a) Sheila feels that she should find out who's responsible for the woman's death.

b) Lenin's strong leadership was one reason for his party's success.

c) You'll find that a river's cross profile varies over its course.

d) Paranormal events are things that science can't explain, such as ghosts.

e) I've never seen 'Macbeth' on stage, but I'd love to see it.

Q7 a) I found the saucepan lid and re-covered the food.

b) The pro-democracy movement was unsuccessful.

c) The pre-1941 agreement was broken.

d) I had to de-ice the car windscreen before I left work.

e) The troops re-entered the city at night.

Q8 a) "Good morning, sir," called the greengrocer.

b) The King said, "You have my word."

c) "Can I see some evidence?" he asked.

d) She said, "The Earth spins on an axis."

e) Luke said, "I liked the main character."

f) Joseph whispered, "It's time to go."

g) "Where shall we go for lunch?" she asked.

h) Everyone shouted, "Hooray!"

Q9 a) The Earth's population is increasing and we're running out of many resources.

b) Jesus fed 5 000 people using a young boy's five loaves and two fish.

c) Martin Luther King campaigned for African Americans' civil rights.

d) Juliet is a young girl whose family is the enemy of Romeo's family.

e) The Inspector lets the Birlings grow suspicious of each other.

f) Nobody's going to remember, so we'll have to do it ourselves.

Q10 a) Some people argue that being a good person has its own rewards.

b) At the end of the play, it's not clear who the Inspector was.

c) There are ways to reduce traffic and its impacts.

d) When people move to a country, it's called immigration.

e) The Nazi party set up its own armed group called the SA.

f) Muslims won't eat chicken unless it's been butchered in a special way.

g) Each river in a drainage basin has its own valley.

h) Watching film adaptations of books is useful, but it's dangerous to rely on them too much.

Q11 a) Estella, Miss Havisham's adopted daughter, makes Pip feel common.

b) By the end of 1914, there were trenches between Belgium's coast and Switzerland.

c) Flood engineering strategies, such as flood warnings, can reduce the effects of flooding.

d) Christianity, Judaism and Islam all teach that a love of wealth is bad.

e) If you use a wide range of vocabulary, you'll impress the examiner.

f) Macbeth is responsible for the deaths of Banquo, Lady Macduff and King Duncan.

Q12 a) When you read a novel, think about its setting.

b) During the 1960s, anti-war conventions were held in the USA.

c) Nigeria and Cameroon are African countries.

d) "Wait for the others," said Marcus.

e) World War Two (1939-1945) involved many countries.

Section Three — Grammar

Pages 50-51 — Pronouns

Q1 a) There have been major changes in the way we shop in the UK in the last 100 years.

b) Television affects concentration — yours included — so switch it off when revising.

c) Break the information down into smaller pieces, learning them one at a time.

d) The Qur'an states Allah's mercy means he will help us with any problems.

e) Julie gave me the phone number, and I let her have mine.

f) There was no label on the cake, so they didn't know if it was his or hers.

g) The scriptures were written against a different cultural background from ours.

Pronouns that show possession: yours, mine, his, hers, ours

Q2 a) The homework is mine — it belongs to me.

b) The shoes are theirs — they belong to them.

c) The car is yours — it belongs to you.

d) The book is hers — it belongs to her.

e) The dog is ours — it belongs to us.

f) The laptop is his — it belongs to him.

Q3 a) He instructed them to begin work on an A-bomb.

b) It gave him the powers of a dictator.

c) They pray to her and ask her for help.

d) We ran to hers on Monday evening.

Q4 a) Mary is very important to Christians because she gave birth to Jesus.

b) You need to know your facts and you've got to be able to explain them clearly.

c) Earthquakes might seem exciting, but they can be life-threatening.

d) When you read a poem, think about why the poet wrote it.

Q5 a) I respect your beliefs, so you should respect mine.

Answers

b) We ate at my house yesterday — let's eat at <u>yours</u> tonight.

c) That's not our report; it's <u>theirs</u>.

d) They gave a very good presentation, but <u>ours</u> was better.

Q6 a) God made a promise to the people. <u>He</u> said that <u>they</u> would find salvation if <u>they</u> followed <u>his</u> teaching.

b) Martin Luther King used peaceful protests. <u>They</u> enabled <u>him</u> to gain publicity for <u>his</u> cause.

Q7 You should have ticked: **a)** and **e)**.

Page 52 — Who, Which and That

Q1 a) The Earth's surface is made of huge floating plates <u>that</u> are constantly moving.

b) Some people claim Lenin was a quick-thinking leader <u>who</u> inspired his party.

c) A democratic process is any way in <u>which</u> citizens can help to run a country.

d) Around the Earth's core is the mantle, <u>which</u> is semi-molten rock that moves very slowly.

e) Some workers quit, and those <u>that</u> remained were forced to accept a pay cut.

f) Some people were given the job of scaring the pigeons <u>which</u> were causing a nuisance.

g) Through rehabilitation, an offender can learn a trade, <u>which</u> helps their self-esteem.

Q2 a) <u>Who</u> became president in 1921?

b) <u>Which</u> Christian denomination believes in Purgatory?

c) <u>Who</u> was Nelson Mandela?

d) <u>Which</u> American president came up with the Fourteen Points?

Q3 a) Use <u>who</u> when you are talking about people.

b) Use <u>which</u> when you are talking about animals or things.

c) You can use <u>that</u> to refer to things or people.

d) You can use <u>who</u> and <u>which</u> when you ask a question.

Q4 a) Access routes improve communications for people <u>who</u> (OR <u>that</u>) live in that area.

b) Check with your teacher <u>which</u> topics you should revise for your exams.

c) Governments can limit the number of people <u>who</u> (OR <u>that</u>) are allowed to immigrate.

d) Tax credits support parents <u>who</u> (OR <u>that</u>) go back to work after their children are born.

e) Make sure you read and understand the comments <u>which</u> (OR <u>that</u>) are written in red.

f) Christians believe that it was Jesus's death on the cross <u>which</u> (OR <u>that</u>) won the battle against sin.

g) An agnostic is someone <u>who</u> (OR <u>that</u>) believes it's impossible to know whether there's a god.

h) Some believe it was the one-child policy <u>which</u> (OR <u>that</u>) slowed population growth in China.

Page 53 — Who or Whom, Who's or Whose

Q1 a) During the war, Germany's enemy was Britain, <u>whose</u> empire and navy it envied.

b) Austria-Hungary was made up of 10 nationalities, many of <u>whom</u> wanted independence.

c) The chief priests and elders asked Jesus on <u>whose</u> authority he was acting.

d) The person in <u>whom</u> I confided was a close friend of mine.

e) Catholics often pray to a saint on behalf of someone <u>who's</u> suffering.

f) Loans were provided for people <u>whose</u> homes were in danger of being repossessed.

g) Helping those <u>who</u> are in need is seen as a key part of various faiths.

Q2 a) You should have circled: 'who's'
Correct version: Countries <u>whose</u> industries were weak bought American goods.

b) You should have circled: 'whom'
Correct version: The sources disagree about <u>who</u> started the fire.

c) You should have circled: 'who'
Correct version: The photo shows two men, both of <u>whom</u> were politicians.

d) You should have circled: 'whose'
Correct version: The clergy consists of anyone <u>who's</u> been ordained.

Q3 a) Governments make alliances with foreign leaders <u>who</u> share their ideas.

b) A hypocrite is a person <u>whose</u> actions don't match what they say.

c) During a flood, rescue boats are usually sent to help people <u>who</u> are stranded.

d) The campsite was so dark, I couldn't tell which tent belonged to <u>whom</u>.

e) The Bible states divorce is only permitted to someone <u>whose</u> partner has been unfaithful.

f) Critics say it is hard to guess <u>who's</u> going to win the film award.

g) At funerals, the life of the person <u>who's</u> died is usually celebrated.

h) The police want to find the witness <u>who's</u> wanted in connection with the crime.

i) After the argument, no one could remember who said what to <u>whom</u>.

Page 54 — Verbs

Q1 You should have circled the words in bold and underlined the words that are underlined:

a) Priests <u>are</u> in charge of Catholic worship and education in their parish.

b) Visitors <u>damage</u> forests by causing erosion and disturbing wildlife.

c) Scientists usually <u>publish</u> their findings in scientific journals.

d) Warm, moist air from the tropics <u>meets</u> cold, dry air from the poles.

e) Many people in poor countries <u>depend</u> on farming.

f) In most Muslim communities, **parents** <u>search</u> for suitable partners for their children.

g) The Qur'an <u>describes</u> Jahannam as a place of scorching fire, hot winds and black smoke.

h) Military forces <u>need</u> the best available equipment for their troops.

Q2 a) During droughts, soil, which is sometimes made up of clay and rock particles, <u>dries</u> out.

Answers

b) An electrical phenomenon, such as static electricity or lightning, <u>is</u> fairly commonplace.
c) First aid training, designed to teach life-saving skills, <u>focuses</u> on a variety of things.
d) A layer of undergrowth, including brambles and mosses, <u>covers</u> the entire area.
e) The community of several thousand people <u>rejects</u> the proposal.
f) Many scientists, such as Stephen Hawking, <u>believe</u> science governs the universe.
g) Discriminatory behaviour, including racism and ageism, <u>contradicts</u> our ethics.
h) The recruitment process, contrary to recent criticisms, <u>plays</u> an important role.

Q3 a) <u>Bananas contain</u> roughly fourteen grams of sugar.
b) Religious <u>people</u> usually <u>go</u> to church regularly.
c) <u>Cyclists ride</u> along the road or the cycle path.
d) <u>The currents are</u> faster on the outside of the bend.
e) <u>The politicians have</u> many supporters.

Page 55 — Forming the Present Tense

Q1 a) he <u>flies</u>
b) she <u>confesses</u>
c) Mike <u>argues</u>
d) it <u>cries</u>
e) Julie <u>travels</u>
f) it <u>relies</u>
g) she <u>addresses</u>
h) he <u>replies</u>

Q2 a) Some of the players <u>enjoy</u> taking penalties.
b) The government <u>employs</u> many civil servants.
c) Jesus <u>catches</u> up with his disciples' boat by walking across the water.
d) The roots of a desert plant usually <u>reach</u> deep underground to find water.
e) Our family <u>tries</u> to have great holidays on a budget.
f) The Nile <u>stretches</u> north from East Africa to the Mediterranean.
g) David <u>studies</u> the constellations in the sky.
h) The jury <u>believes</u> the accused is innocent.
i) Romeo <u>hurries</u> back to Verona when he thinks Juliet is dead.
j) The rising sea level <u>destroys</u> coastal habitats.

Q3

Verb	I	You (singular)	He/She/It	We	You (plural)	They
to be	am	are	is	are	are	are
to have	have	have	has	have	have	have

Q4 a) The Earth's surface <u>is</u> separated into tectonic plates.
b) In an Orthodox wedding, crowns <u>are</u> placed on the heads of the bride and groom.
c) A worker on strike told the interviewer, "I <u>am</u> unhappy with the working conditions."
d) Macbeth and Banquo <u>are</u> soldiers in the Scottish army.
e) Christians believe that we <u>are</u> all responsible for caring for the planet.
f) The Friar <u>is</u> persuaded to help Romeo and Juliet.

Pages 56-57 — Forming -ing Verbs

Q1 a) I <u>am writing</u>.
b) You <u>are writing</u>.
c) He <u>is writing</u>.
d) We <u>are writing</u>.
e) You <u>are writing</u>.
f) They <u>are writing</u>.

Q2 a) I <u>was lying</u>.
b) You <u>were lying</u>.
c) She <u>was lying</u>.
d) We <u>were lying</u>.
e) You <u>were lying</u>.
f) They <u>were lying</u>.

Q3 a) The poster shows that the soldiers <u>were driving</u> the enemy away.
b) Increased traffic meant the narrow roads <u>were developing</u> potholes.
c) During hyperinflation, people <u>were buying</u> items with bags full of money.
d) One witness said the ground <u>was shaking</u> violently during the earthquake.
e) The fans <u>were applauding</u> enthusiastically, so the band played more songs.
f) In the 1930s, women <u>were embracing</u> roles traditionally fulfilled by men.
g) I <u>was debating</u> whether or not to apply for the job vacancy.
h) The Labour MP <u>was appealing</u> to the Conservative MP for a straight answer.
i) Protesters <u>were targeting</u> the main government buildings.

Q4 a) He <u>is addressing</u> the congregation.
b) Aid workers <u>are travelling</u> to Africa.
c) The Earth's plates <u>are moving</u>.
d) I <u>am helping</u> those in need.
e) The event <u>is promoting</u> justice.
f) You <u>are complicating</u> matters.
g) Builders <u>are levelling</u> the road.
h) They <u>are considering</u> the outcome.

Q5 a) People <u>are beginning</u> to recycle more of their rubbish.
b) I <u>am visiting</u> the site of a World War One battlefield.
c) Melika <u>is shaking</u> her piggy bank to find another coin.
d) The cheeky children <u>are annoying</u> the teacher.
e) The men and women <u>are dancing</u> separately.
f) Army leaders do not believe their troops <u>are winning</u> the war.
g) The risk of coastal flooding <u>is becoming</u> greater.
h) The airline <u>is doubling</u> the number of flights to Poland.

Q6 In the boardroom, the managers <u>were discussing</u> whether to alter the menu in the canteen, but not everyone <u>was paying</u> attention. Mr May <u>was tapping</u> away on his phone, whilst Miss Cross <u>was staring</u> out of the window. The two new accountants <u>were chatting</u> and Mrs Gray <u>was tidying</u> her handbag.

Q7 a) The refugees of war <u>were fleeing</u> from the threat of violence.
b) Don't forget to say which religion you <u>are referring</u> to.
c) Air-raid sirens warned citizens that an attack <u>was coming</u>.
d) A group of scientists <u>are challenging</u> the Big Bang theory.
e) The climber <u>is tying</u> knots in the rope.
f) The driver <u>was breaking</u> the speed limit.
g) Emergency aid helps those who <u>are dying</u> from starvation.
h) Victory banners and flags <u>were flapping</u> on the rooftops.

Answers

Pages 58-59 — The Simple Past

Q1
a) became
b) knew
c) celebrated
d) honoured
e) wore
f) behaved
g) dropped
h) hoped
i) hurt
j) slept
k) demanded
l) studied
m) met
n) travelled
o) found
p) died

Q2 You should have circled:
eat, make, steal, have, take, give, see and drink.
The simple past tense forms are:
ate, made, stole, had, took, gave, saw and drank.

Q3
a) Most urbanisation in rich countries <u>occurred</u> during the Industrial Revolution.
b) The doctor <u>admitted</u> to giving the patient a higher dosage of medication.
c) Farmers <u>worried</u> that their crops would fail due to the flood.
d) The former employee was <u>imprisoned</u> for lying in court.
e) The researchers <u>identified</u> several problems with the data.
f) Indochina was a French colony that <u>covered</u> a large area of South-East Asia.
g) Droughts are often <u>accompanied</u> by high temperatures.

Q4
a) Parliament <u>made</u> the law and the courts enforced it.
b) During the Depression, some people <u>fought</u> hard to keep their pride.
c) The Antarctic Treaty is an agreement that <u>came</u> into force in 1961.
d) Mother Teresa <u>was</u> an Albanian Roman Catholic nun.
e) Quaternary industry is sometimes <u>thought</u> of as a part of tertiary industry.
f) All women over 21 <u>got</u> the vote in 1928.
g) Hurricane Mitch <u>hit</u> Nicaragua in 1998.
h) The Depression almost certainly <u>cost</u> Hoover the 1932 election.
i) Anne Frank's diary describes how her family <u>hid</u> from the Nazis.
j) The Reformation <u>began</u> when Martin Luther challenged the Pope's authority.
k) After the storm, exports of rice <u>went</u> down as crops were damaged.

Q5
a) The company <u>withheld</u> some information.
b) We <u>did</u> our best at the Summer Championships.
c) They <u>transferred</u> money between accounts.
d) Fairtrade schemes <u>paid</u> farmers a fair price.

Q6 A theatre group <u>put</u> on a production of 'My Fair Lady' last night. The cast <u>sold</u> every single ticket before the show, which <u>beat</u> all expectations. The local press <u>reviewed</u> the performance. One critic <u>wrote</u>, "It's not surprising the play <u>brought</u> in a large crowd — the actors <u>sang</u> beautifully and <u>caught</u> the audience's full attention."

Pages 60-61 — The Past Tense with 'Have'

Q1
a) They <u>have heard</u> an explosion.
b) You <u>have rented</u> a caravan.
c) He <u>has explained</u> it.
d) I <u>have left</u> the meeting early.
e) We <u>have decided</u> to go.
f) She <u>has promised</u> to do her best.
g) It <u>has become</u> apparent that we're losing.
h) We <u>have taken</u> the books back to the library.

Q2
a) I <u>have gone</u>
b) you <u>have told</u>
c) he <u>has bitten</u>
d) they <u>have won</u>
e) we <u>have blown</u>
f) she <u>has built</u>
g) I <u>have chosen</u>
h) we <u>have come</u>
i) it <u>has cost</u>
j) you <u>have drawn</u>
k) it <u>has left</u>
l) it <u>has fallen</u>
m) you <u>have given</u>
n) he <u>has forgotten</u>
o) they <u>have drunk</u>
p) she <u>has heard</u>
q) I <u>have fled</u>
r) we <u>have frozen</u>
s) I <u>have grown</u>
t) they <u>have known</u>

Q3
a) They <u>have been</u> fighting a lot.
b) You <u>have gone</u> the wrong way.
c) I <u>have done</u> the washing-up.
d) We <u>have seen</u> the film.
e) She <u>has taken</u> the car.
f) Jane <u>has been</u> to France.
g) He <u>has done</u> his homework.
h) I <u>have made</u> a mistake.

Q4
a) His friends <u>have forgiven</u> him for his mistake.
b) The rain <u>has fallen</u> over the hills.
c) The factory workers <u>have done</u> lots of overtime.
d) The choir <u>has sung</u> the hymns.
e) The urban population <u>has grown</u> quickly.

Q5
a) In times <u>of</u> recession, people tend to cut back on luxuries.
b) No organisation could <u>have</u> stopped leaders like Mussolini or Hitler peacefully.
c) It would <u>have</u> taken years for the country to pay off its debt.
d) Prayer can be thought <u>of</u> as a conversation with God.
e) There are many reasons why businesses might <u>have</u> rejected the deal.
f) Wedding guests are asked if they know <u>of</u> any reason why the couple should not marry.

Q6
a) The birds <u>have eaten</u> the seeds planted by the farmer.
b) The players <u>have lost</u> the game and are returning home.
c) If the criminal <u>has broken</u> the law, the punishment will be severe.
d) Roger <u>has beaten</u> the eggs and is now sifting the flour.
e) The aid workers <u>have driven</u> 2 000 miles to reach Syria.
f) Some prisoners <u>have forgotten</u> what it's like to be free citizens.
g) Your opinion may be affected by what you <u>have read</u>.
h) The Prime Minister <u>has spoken</u> to the German Chancellor.

Answers

i) The First and Second World Wars <u>have taught</u> us many lessons.
j) Limiting visitor access <u>has kept</u> the impact of tourism low.

Pages 62-63 — Negatives

Q1 You should have underlined:
a) There <u>doesn't</u> seem to be <u>no</u> reason for the conflict.
b) <u>Nothing</u> could prepare them for what happened.
c) We <u>don't</u> know <u>none</u> of the people over there.
d) There's <u>nowhere</u> quite like the Shetland Islands.
e) I am <u>not</u> telling <u>nobody</u> about my new hobby.
f) The American people <u>never</u> accepted the Treaty of Versailles.
You should have ticked: **b)**, **d)**, **f)**
You should have crossed: **a)**, **c)**, **e)**
The correct sentences are:
a) There doesn't seem to be <u>any</u> reason for the conflict.
OR There seems to be <u>no</u> reason for the conflict.
c) We don't know <u>any</u> of the people over there.
OR We know <u>none</u> of the people over there.
e) I am not telling <u>anybody</u> about my new hobby.
OR I am telling <u>nobody</u> about my new hobby.

Q2 a) The government didn't accept <u>any</u> foreign aid.
b) It was called the Cold War because there wasn't <u>any</u> direct fighting.
c) The governor <u>didn't</u> discuss the matter with <u>anybody</u>.
d) They decided not to share <u>any</u> information with <u>anyone</u>.
e) We want to donate some old clothes, but we don't have <u>any</u>.
f) Wild kangaroos can't be found <u>anywhere</u> in the UK.
g) There isn't <u>anything</u> we can do to turn back time.
h) There's no chance of finding <u>anything</u> useful in a blank book.

Q3 a) There <u>aren't any</u> sharks in the lake.
OR There are <u>no</u> sharks in the lake.
b) I <u>haven't</u> got <u>a</u> problem with that.
OR I have got <u>no</u> problem with that.
c) He <u>isn't</u> the boss — I am.
d) Kim <u>hasn't</u> seen the new play.
e) We <u>haven't</u> got time to go there.
f) Tim <u>isn't ever</u> going to change.
OR Tim <u>is never</u> going to change.
g) You <u>haven't</u> met <u>anybody</u> like Olga.
OR You <u>have never</u> met <u>anybody</u> like Olga.

Q4

She <u>doesn't</u> know.	They <u>don't</u> know.
We <u>don't</u> know.	You <u>don't</u> know.
He <u>doesn't</u> know.	It <u>doesn't</u> know.
I <u>don't</u> know.	

Q5 a) Predicting a volcanic eruption <u>doesn't</u> stop buildings being destroyed.
b) Many hospitals in poorer countries <u>don't</u> have enough supplies.
c) <u>Don't</u> take sources at face value — look at what a source really means.
d) I <u>don't</u> judge people by how they look, but by how they behave.
e) Preparation <u>doesn't</u> guarantee safety from a flood.

f) Atheists <u>don't</u> believe in a god.
g) We <u>don't</u> usually rely on others for help.
h) In the Bible, Jesus <u>doesn't</u> just talk about forgiveness.

Q6 a) The UK <u>doesn't have</u> a rainforest.
b) Unemployed people <u>don't</u> work.
c) We <u>don't</u> complain about the noise.
d) I <u>don't</u> feel very well.
e) Malcolm <u>doesn't attend</u> Mass.
f) Our horse <u>doesn't like</u> carrots.
g) The manager <u>doesn't agree</u> with us.
h) Money <u>doesn't grow</u> on trees.
i) Vegetarians <u>don't eat</u> meat.
j) Tim and Tina <u>don't have</u> a pet.

Pages 64-65 — Staying in the Right Tense

Q1 You should have ticked: **a)** and **c)**.
You should have crossed: **b)** and **d)**.

Q2 a) Last Saturday, there was a torrential downpour and many towns <u>flooded</u>.
b) In today's world, many people live and <u>work</u> in terrible conditions.
c) When the boats landed yesterday, the troops <u>swam</u> ashore.
d) By this time tomorrow, the two leaders <u>will have met</u> to discuss the crisis and will have resolved it.
e) Last month, the town hall clock broke, so the mayor <u>fixed</u> it and reset the time.
f) Environmentalists will sign a petition next week and they <u>will post</u> it to their MP.
g) I followed the plan in my last exam, and I <u>left</u> time to check my work.

Q3 The Model T was a motorcar that was first produced in 1908. It <u>became</u> the first affordable motorcar that <u>made</u> it possible for middle-class American families to travel freely. Henry Ford <u>produced</u> this vehicle using assembly line production, and by 1927 he <u>saw</u> the fifteen millionth Model T roll off his assembly line. In 1914, Ford <u>decided</u> to only make this model available in black, which perhaps <u>helped</u> to keep production costs down.

Q4 a) vi d) iii
b) iv e) ii
c) i f) v

Q5 a) Some people live in villages and <u>commute</u> to work in urban areas.
b) German forces had orders to pull out if the French army <u>moved</u> in.
c) In 2006, Zambia <u>had</u> enough money to offer free health care.
d) The rabbi will read from the Torah and he <u>will give</u> a sermon.
e) We will clear out your room and Dad <u>will take</u> your things to the tip.
f) The cross is a Christian symbol which <u>represents</u> Jesus's crucifixion.
g) The world's population is increasing — it <u>is growing</u> rapidly.
h) In 2004, ten eastern European countries <u>joined</u> the EU.
i) The nature reserve <u>attracted</u> thousands of visitors in 2011.

Answers

j) Within days, lots of money had been pledged and work <u>had begun</u>.

k) My workload is shrinking — the pile on my desk <u>is getting</u> smaller.

l) Cody <u>hid</u> Brad's car keys and didn't tell him.

m) A conundrum <u>is</u> a confusing or difficult problem.

Q6 a) The tsunami destroyed towns and 1.7 million people <u>lost</u> their homes.

b) Currently, we are raising money and we <u>are encouraging</u> people to buy Fairtrade products.

c) By the end of May, the army had interrogated 100 soldiers and it <u>had</u> imprisoned 142 others.

d) The Last Post ceremony takes place every day at 8 pm in Ypres and <u>attracts</u> lots of visitors.

e) We will announce the reforms tomorrow, but it is expected that the workers <u>will reject</u> them.

Pages 66-67 — Paragraphs

Q1 Paragraph 1: a, <u>d</u>, <u>f</u>, <u>j</u>   Paragraph 2: b, <u>e</u>, g, <u>k</u>
Paragraph 3: c, <u>h</u>, <u>i</u>, <u>l</u>

Q2 The first tennis championships at Wimbledon took place in 1877, when twenty-two men paid one pound and one shilling to take part. These participants were told to bring their own rackets and to wear shoes without heels. Balls, however, were provided. // In 1884, women were permitted to play in their own championships. However, play could only begin once the men's singles had been completed. // A female player from the United States called May Sutton became the first overseas entrant to be crowned champion. She won the tournament in 1905 and went on to win it again in 1907. May's entry showed that international players were willing to travel to London to take part in the championships. // The popularity of tennis tournaments spread far and wide, and today tournaments take place across the globe. This means professional players must be willing to travel long distances and thereby dedicate their lives to the game. As one famous player states, "For me, playing tennis is not just a career; it is a way of life."

Q3 At the end of the Second World War, Germany and Berlin were divided into zones shared between the Allies. Russia controlled East Germany and East Berlin, whilst America, France and Britain controlled West Germany and West Berlin. // As time went by, relations between Russia and America deteriorated, and the Cold War began. The term 'Cold War' came about because there wasn't any direct fighting between these two powers. Russia and America were, however, making plans and alliances that the other disagreed with. // Over in East Germany and East Berlin, communism firmly gripped the nation, whilst capitalism was the ruling ideology in western parts. A communist lifestyle did not appeal to most citizens, and many decided to flee to the West through Berlin. // In 1961, the Berlin Wall was put up to prevent East Germans from escaping to the West. This consisted of a concrete barrier with barbed wire and machine gun watchtowers.

Q4 Volcanic lightning is when lightning is produced in a volcanic plume. It's a rare weather phenomenon where two forces of nature, a volcanic eruption and lightning, can be seen at once. Volcanic lightning has been witnessed at almost 200 eruptions over the past 200 years. // Dr Higman, a geologist, has photographed dramatic images of volcanic lightning. His photos depict an eruption at Mount Redoubt in Alaska. // On 17th April 2010, volcanic lightning occurred at Eyjafjallajökull, Iceland. This particular volcanic eruption began on 14th April and became famous for causing major disruption to air travel across Europe.

Q5 a) I started the second paragraph because the text mentions a new <u>person</u>.

b) I started the third paragraph because the text mentions a new <u>time</u>.

Pages 68-71 — Mixed Practice

Q1 a) A donor country is a country that <u>gives</u> aid to another country.

b) During the tournament, one team won and seven teams <u>lost</u>.

c) We carried out some research and <u>compiled</u> all the evidence.

d) The population is shrinking because people <u>are having</u> fewer children.

e) He had told him that he <u>had passed</u> his driving test.

f) They approved the plans and the building work <u>started</u>.

g) I tolerate animal experimentation, but only if it <u>benefits</u> mankind.

h) The forest has gone and the number of endangered species <u>has risen</u>.

i) We were listening whilst the mayor <u>was speaking</u>.

j) The sun is shining, the birds are singing and people <u>are sunbathing</u>.

Q2

simple past tense	past tense with 'have'
You rode your horse.	I <u>have ridden</u> my horse.
He <u>ran</u> 10 miles.	We have run 10 miles.
Her foot <u>swelled</u>.	My foot has swollen.
The dog woke up.	The cat <u>has woken</u> up.
We <u>mowed</u> the lawn.	They have mown the lawn.

Q3 a) She <u>doesn't have</u> a car.

b) We <u>don't</u> work during the day.

c) I <u>don't</u> play the tuba.

d) He <u>doesn't believe</u> in fairies.

e) They <u>don't</u> work together.

f) Sam <u>doesn't go</u> to the gym.

Q4 a) The party had many supporters, many of <u>whom</u> pledged generous donations.

b) Fold mountain areas have lots of high mountains, <u>which</u> are very rocky with steep slopes.

c) Hitler was a German leader <u>whose</u> hatred of the Jews had catastrophic consequences.

d) Most people have their own opinion about <u>who's</u> been the best president to date.

Answers

e) Upland areas in the Alps are used to farm goats <u>that</u> provide milk, cheese and meat.

f) It's difficult to say <u>who</u> was responsible for the Reichstag Fire.

Q5 You should have ticked: **a)**, **d)**, **f)**, **i)**
The correct sentences are:

b) I <u>have spoken</u> to him already.
OR I <u>spoke</u> to him already.

c) He <u>has stolen</u> a pencil.
OR He <u>stole</u> a pencil.

e) We <u>have written</u> a letter.
OR We <u>wrote</u> a letter.

g) It could <u>have gone</u> wrong.
OR It could <u>go</u> wrong.

h) The dough <u>has risen</u>.
OR The dough <u>rose</u>.

j) She has <u>forgotten</u> her money.
OR She <u>forgot</u> her money.

Q6 a) By the end of Act Three, Scene One, Romeo has <u>been</u> banished from Verona.

b) In some religions, suffering is <u>seen</u> as a test of faith.

c) Some developing countries are <u>seeing</u> massive industrial growth.

d) Mussolini had <u>been</u> made Prime Minister in 1922 after threatening to march on Rome.

e) A lot of Spain's energy is <u>being</u> produced using wind turbines.

f) After the Russian Revolution, communism was <u>seen</u> as a serious threat.

g) Some ecosystems are <u>being</u> threatened by poorly-managed tourism.

Q7

verb	present tense with 'ing'	past tense with 'ing'
to stop	you <u>are stopping</u>	they <u>were stopping</u>
to panic	I <u>am panicking</u>	he <u>was panicking</u>
to create	we <u>are creating</u>	I <u>was creating</u>
to party	she <u>is partying</u>	you <u>were partying</u>
to progress	they <u>are progressing</u>	it <u>was progressing</u>

Q8 Advent marks the start of the Christian year, and <u>begins</u> four Sundays before Christmas. It <u>is</u> a period of preparation for Christmas. People light Advent candles in homes and churches, and children may <u>use</u> Advent calendars to count off the days until Christmas. Christians celebrate Christmas on December 25th, but December 26th <u>is</u> also a bank holiday in England.

Q9 a) Most people believe a woman should be able to choose whom <u>she</u> marries.

b) Charles Dickens was 58 years old when <u>he</u> died in 1870.

c) I've applied for the job and <u>I</u> am waiting to hear that they've received my CV.

d) When the troops retreated, <u>they</u> didn't have time to get back into their trenches.

e) I don't really mind whether we take your car or <u>mine</u> to the horse show.

f) In your revision of this topic, make sure <u>you</u> learn all of the key facts.

g) Free will allows us to choose whether <u>we</u> do good or evil with our lives.

Q10 a) There's never been <u>any</u> trouble in this area.
OR There's been <u>no</u> trouble in this area.

b) There <u>doesn't</u> seem to be any reason to go to war.
OR There seems to be <u>no</u> reason to go to war.

c) We <u>haven't</u> discussed a solution to the problem yet.

d) The weapons weren't <u>anywhere</u> to be seen.
OR The weapons were <u>nowhere</u> to be seen.

e) I <u>don't</u> intend to join in the protest.

f) They don't know <u>anything</u> about the benefits system.
OR They know <u>nothing</u> about the benefits system.

Q11 a) In parts of Australia, armed robbery <u>carries</u> a maximum sentence of 25 years.

b) Judaism <u>teaches</u> that we have free will and are able to choose what we do.

c) 'Bulldozing' is when the ice of a glacier <u>pushes</u> loose material in front of it.

d) The interviewer <u>quizzes</u> celebrities about their professional and private lives.

e) When a chef <u>fries</u> an egg, the proteins in the egg white move vigorously.

f) Condensation <u>occurs</u> as warm air rises, causing rain clouds to develop.

g) In rainforests, the soil isn't very fertile as heavy rain <u>washes</u> nutrients away.

h) The Jewish faith <u>stresses</u> the idea that good can come out of terrible suffering.

i) A sensible pupil <u>practises</u> exam-style questions during their revision.

Q12 a) chose **g)** cut **m)** broke
b) bound **h)** bent **n)** froze
c) fell **i)** drew **o)** held
d) built **j)** grew **p)** left
e) dealt **k)** fed **q)** shook
f) felt **l)** bled **r)** kept

Section Four — Proofreading

Page 72 — Checking Your Spelling

Q1 Christian Aid was set up after World War II to help refugees. It now works <u>globally</u> to <u>relieve</u> poverty. It raises money through <u>donations</u>, events and <u>collections</u>. Most of Christian Aid's work is in <u>development</u>. Projects set up by Christian Aid focus on poor <u>sanitation</u>, education and healthcare, as well as encouraging the use of birth control. The organisation also aims to change <u>government</u> policy to reduce the <u>suffering</u> of the world's poor, e.g. through debt <u>relief</u>.

Q2 You should have circled: acording, essentialy, catergory, maintenence, vareity and successfull. The correct spellings are: according, essentially, category, maintenance, variety and successful.

Q3 As a country becomes more <u>developed</u>, its population often increases. One reason is that the <u>medical</u> <u>facilities</u> in the country improve, so its patients have better access to doctors and the <u>medicines</u> they need. Also, life <u>expectancy</u> increases because people have better <u>nutrition</u>. However, a growing population can lead to <u>housing</u> problems and rising <u>unemployment</u> because <u>there</u> are not <u>sufficient</u> jobs.

Answers

Page 73 — Checking Your Punctuation

Q1 a) Air pollution and rapid urbanisation cause problems in Beijing and <u>m</u>umbai.

b) During Ramadan, Muslims<u>'</u> fast during the daylight hours (between sunrise and sunset).

c) The exam question asked students why the Great Depression occurred in America<u>?</u>

d) Kenya's economy depends on tourism, agriculture, farming and<u>,</u> mining.

e) In 'Macbeth', the country's well-being is linked to that of <u>it's</u> king.

f) Tourism can benefit local industries<u>,</u> that supply tourist attractions or restaurants.

Q2 a) 'Animal Farm', written by George Orwell<u>,</u> is based on historical events.

b) There were many anti<u>-</u>war protests during the early 21st century.

c) Think about these aspects of the poem<u>:</u> subject, form, rhyme and rhythm.

d) After a volcanic eruption, there is a big crater <u>(</u>a caldera) left behind.

e) In the 1930s, Italy and Japan both invaded other countries<u>'</u> territories.

f) "There are a lot of employees off sick," said the manager, "and I feel ill today."

g) Although the Allies won the war<u>,</u> many British people did not celebrate.

Q3 People<u>'</u>s attitudes changed as the war went on<u>.</u> In 1914, there was enthusiasm for the war<u>,</u> but by 1918, people were disillusioned with it<u>.</u> Propaganda (persuasive words or images<u>)</u> was used to encourage men to join the army. Lord <u>K</u>itchener appeared on a poster with the words, <u>"</u>Your country needs you" beside him. The government also used <u>its</u> propaganda to raise the country<u>'</u>s morale. By the end<u> </u>of 1917, most British people wanted the war to end.

Page 74 — Checking Your Grammar

Q1 Rivers flood for a variety of reasons. After a long period of rain, the soil <u>becomes</u> saturated, so it is unable to take in any extra water. This means that more water <u>runs</u> off into the rivers and there is a higher risk of flooding. Flooding also <u>occurs</u> when snow and ice melt quickly, because a large quantity of water enters the river system in a very short space of time. If this coincides with a period of heavy or prolonged rainfall, the combination of factors <u>increases</u> the risk of flooding.

Human factors can also <u>cause</u> river flooding, through actions such as deforestation. Trees <u>collect</u> water on their leaves which then evaporates, and they draw up water through their roots, so there is less water in the ground. If there <u>are</u> fewer trees, the water runs off into rivers, causing them to rise.

Q2 a) 'Pride and Prejudice' was <u>wrote</u> by Jane Austen and published in 1813. Correct: <u>written</u>

b) Juliet drinks the potion that Friar Laurence gives <u>hers</u> and falls asleep. Correct: <u>her</u>

c) After the rain, the water in the river <u>were</u> rising at an alarming rate. Correct: <u>was</u>

d) Harry and <u>me</u> worked on a History project about Queen Victoria. Correct: <u>I</u>

e) Lady Macbeth says she would <u>of</u> killed Duncan herself if she could. Correct: <u>have</u>

f) The soul is the spiritual part of a person that <u>ain't</u> a physical substance. Correct: <u>isn't</u>

Q3 At the beginning of 'Animal Farm', Old Major describes a vision he has in <u>which</u> the animals take over the farm and work for <u>themselves</u>. He criticises Man because he doesn't do <u>any</u> work but he benefits from all the animals' work. Old Major <u>wants</u> all the animals to be equal and <u>he</u> teaches them a song about what life <u>will be</u> like in the future, when the animals rule themselves.

Pages 75-76 — Proofreading

Q1 a) The UK is a democratic <u>society</u>, which <u>means</u> that the <u>British</u> people elect representatives to run the country. In the UK, every adult <u>citizen</u> has the right to vote (unless they are in prison). During the 19th <u>century</u>, <u>several</u> reform acts had <u>given</u> most men the vote<u>.</u>

However, in the early 1900s, women still <u>couldn't</u> vote in national elections. People thought that women belonged at home, and it <u>was</u> the man's role to take part in public affairs. After many years<u> </u>of protests, women <u>finally</u> <u>achieved</u> equal voting rights to men in 1928.

b) Christians believe that they have a duty to be <u>charitable</u> and show love<u> </u>to other people. 'Charity' means any help that is <u>given</u> freely to other people. Here are some things people can give: time, such as visiting the elderly; effort, <u>which</u> could involve building a <u>community</u> centre; and material things, for instance, <u>donating</u> money.

Some religious groups<u> </u>are dedicated to <u>relieving</u> suffering among the poor and sick<u>.</u> Mother Teresa devoted herself to helping people in Calcutta, <u>India.</u> <u>She</u> set up a religious order <u>whose</u> members now <u>help</u> the poor all over the world<u>.</u>

Q2 a) There <u>are</u> many features <u>which</u> (OR <u>that</u>) make up spoken language<u>.</u> When someone speaks<u>,</u> their accent and dialect (the way they pronounce certain words<u>)</u> can reveal <u>a lot</u> about <u>their</u> background. The situation can also <u>affect</u> the <u>language</u> that people <u>use</u>. For example, if <u>you're</u> in a restaurant, you might use set language routines, such as, "Could I have the bill, please<u>?</u>" Also, some people <u>don't</u> always say what they mean, so you might need to look for <u>implied</u> meanings.

b) Food <u>is</u> important to many <u>religions</u>, especially during certain <u>festivals</u>. Christians<u>,</u> Muslims and Jews all believe that God is the <u>creator</u>, and so <u>ultimately</u> all food comes from God. One of the <u>most important</u> events in the Jewish calendar is called Passover; this is a time when Jews eat <u>specific</u> foods. Yeast is <u>forbidden</u>, so Jews eat unleavened bread (bread made without yeast<u>).</u>

Fasting (not eating for a period of time<u>)</u> is part of many religions <u>too</u>. For example, <u>Muslims</u> fast between <u>sunrise</u> and sunset during the month of Ramadan.

EGW42